Atlas of Butterflies
IN BERKSHIRE, BUCKINGHAMSHIRE & OXFORDSHIRE

Jim Asher, Nick Bowles, Jan Haseler, Grahame Hawker, Peter Ogden, David Roy, Richard Soulsby and Mike Wilkins

Butterfly
Conservation

piscespublications

Upper Thames Branch

First published 2016 by Pisces Publications for Butterfly Conservation, Upper Thames Branch.
Pisces Publications is the imprint of NatureBureau.

British Library-in-Publication Data
A catalogue record for this book is available from the British Library.

ISBN 978-1-874357-73-5

Designed and produced by NatureBureau, 36 Kingfisher Court, Hambridge Road, Newbury, Berkshire RG14 5SJ
www.naturebureau.co.uk

Printed and bound by Henry Ling Ltd., Dorchester, Dorset

CONTENTS

INTRODUCTION

The threats to butterflies are probably more widely acknowledged than ever before but many people still have little idea of the level of threat, the threats themselves, or potential solutions to them. To counter this, the aims of this book, the fourth describing the numbers and distributions of butterflies in the Upper Thames Branch (UTB) of Butterfly Conservation (covering Berkshire, Buckinghamshire and Oxfordshire) are:

- to provide up-to-date distribution maps and details of flight periods to help find butterflies locally;
- to highlight declines or expansions in distribution, with commentary on possible contributory causes;
- to say thank you to the dedicated butterfly recorders who contribute to our survey schemes, recognising how their efforts contribute to the bigger picture.

We wish to further raise awareness of the threats to butterflies and their changing nature. We will draw attention to altered priorities, to some local successes, and promote actions that promise a more stable future for these threatened insects.

In 30 years our region has lost 10% of its butterfly species

The first formal review of UTB's butterflies was in 1985, when Caroline and David Steel published *Butterflies of Berkshire, Buckinghamshire & Oxfordshire*. That book described 48 species as breeding within our three counties. Three of those species (High Brown Fritillary, Small Pearl-bordered Fritillary and Pearl-bordered Fritillary) are now acknowledged to have been lost between 1980 and 1995. Two more species seem to have reached the brink of local extinction during the compilation of this most recent atlas: Marsh Fritillary (although adults were seen in 2014, there is no evidence that they bred) and Wall which was, until relatively recently, widely distributed throughout our region.

Currently, we know of 43 species that breed in Berkshire, Buckinghamshire and Oxfordshire. Their futures are perhaps more secure than those of the species we have already lost, as those most threatened are largely found on nature reserves where efforts are made to use our ever improving knowledge of their needs to maintain them. Even species that are found outside nature reserves are in a somewhat better position because of our knowledge of the factors that determine their success and failure and the implementation of that knowledge by many other organisations. For example: Railtrack is working to mitigate impacts to butterflies and moths during their re-opening of the line between Oxford and Bletchley; and Cherwell District Council is striving to conserve important habitats whilst providing new homes around Bicester.

We often divide species into two classes: *habitat specialists*, which are generally rather rare and localised, usually because sites meeting their habitat requirements are increasingly rare and isolated in our countryside, and *wider countryside species*, which are not restricted to special semi-natural habitats and are generally distributed across our landscapes. Within Upper Thames region, these are shown in the tables opposite.

Most of the loss of occupied sites and most of the severe declines in distribution and abundance, have been among the *habitat specialists*, for which the maintenance of their ideal habitat is crucial. But we must not be complacent about the *wider countryside species*: without due care they could in time become more restricted and localised, and ultimately lost from the region. The Wall is one example of a previously widely distributed species that has undergone a severe and unexpected decline within three decades.

Habitat specialists (grouped by family):
Dingy Skipper
Grizzled Skipper
Silver-spotted Skipper
Wood White
Small Heath
Marbled White
Grayling
Silver-washed Fritillary
Dark Green Fritillary
White Admiral
Purple Emperor
Marsh Fritillary
Duke of Burgundy
Brown Hairstreak
Green Hairstreak
White-letter Hairstreak
Black Hairstreak
Small Blue
Silver-studded Blue
Adonis Blue
Chalkhill Blue

We believe that publication of the earlier butterfly atlases within the UTB area and the national account in *The Millennium Atlas of Butterflies in Britain and Ireland* have contributed to a greater understanding of the plight of these creatures, which, in turn, has led to greater efforts to conserve them (and a suite of associated wildlife). The substantial increase in recorders contributing to this most recent *Atlas of the Butterflies of Berkshire, Buckinghamshire and Oxfordshire* indicates a far wider concern and a determination to protect what remains.

To get the most from this book, we suggest you consider it as a companion to the earlier Pisces Publication books on the same theme (particularly *The Butterflies of Berkshire, Buckinghamshire and Oxfordshire* (1984) and the *State of Butterflies in Berkshire, Buckinghamshire and Oxfordshire* (2005)).

We do not intend to repeat much of the background information (for instance, guidelines on identification and typical behaviours of individual species) as they have been covered extensively in those and other publications. Instead, we wish to highlight the dynamic nature of our butterfly populations as they respond to challenges and opportunities in habitats that are created, managed or destroyed. We also hope that the atlas will encourage those with a growing interest in butterflies to find (and photograph if they wish) the rarer species. This is aided by maps of their present and former distributions, together with a list (page 70) of some of the best publicly accessible sites at which a number of the less common species can be found.

Wider countryside species (grouped by family):

Essex Skipper
Small Skipper
Large Skipper

Orange-tip
Large White
Small White
Green-veined White
Clouded Yellow
Brimstone

Wall
Speckled Wood
Ringlet
Meadow Brown
Gatekeeper
Red Admiral
Painted Lady
Peacock
Small Tortoiseshell
Comma

Small Copper
Purple Hairstreak
Holly Blue
Brown Argus
Common Blue

ACKNOWLEDGEMENTS

We are very pleased to acknowledge the financial assistance of generous gifts from David Redhead, Tony Croft and Phil Penson towards the production and mailing costs of this publication. David was a pivotal figure and a driving force in Upper Thames Branch for many years until he moved to South Wales, from where he still follows our progress – and keeps us up to date with his new local patch, too. Tony and Phil still live locally and continue to monitor sensitive sites and key populations, contributing a large number of records each year.

We are grateful to a number of organisations who have kindly shared data with us and allowed us to use it in this publication:

- Buckinghamshire and Milton Keynes Environmental Records Centre (BMERC)
- Thames Valley Environment Records Centre (TVERC)
- Berkshire, Buckinghamshire and Oxfordshire Wildlife Trust (BBOWT)
- Frieth Natural History Society
- Milton Keynes Natural History Society
- Moor Green Lakes Group
- National Trust Biological Survey Team

We are also grateful to the Butterfly Conservation branches in counties bordering Upper Thames Branch who have allowed us to use their records for 2km squares overlapping our common boundaries.

We are currently using the knowledge amassed within Upper Thames Branch to inform the development of a new Regional Action Plan for the South East region of Butterfly Conservation. The data and the findings in this atlas will provide important evidence-based contributions to documents, facts and figures to aid discussions with land managers and policy makers.

The availability and interpretation of the large body of up-to-date records provided by our ever-growing membership is an essential part of this knowledge. We would therefore especially like to thank the many individuals, totalling over 3000 and listed on pages 73–76, who contributed records for this atlas for the period 2005–2014. This atlas would simply not have been possible without the massive help of these many people and we are grateful for their support and for the dedication of whose who contributed to systematic recording and submitted literally thousands of records.

We are grateful also to the following individual coordinators:

- Margaret Price for running the Upper Thames Branch Garden Recording survey, with assistance from Julia Huggins;
- Helen Hyre for running the Upper Thames Branch Churchyard Recording survey;
- All species champions for their contributions to stimulating interest in their species and to this atlas;
- All 10km square champions for coordinating local recording within their squares; and
- Mike Wilkins for coordinating transect recording in our area.

The photographs in this atlas were kindly provided by Jim Asher, Nick Bowles, Tony Gillie, Chris and Pat Dennis (Green Hairstreak *ab. Dennisorum*), and Elaine Ingram (*Surveying the yellow heads of dark mullein, page 66*).

We sincerely hope that some of the pleasure we have derived from compiling this atlas comes through as you read it, and that it stands as a tribute to the efforts of all our contributors. Any such publication reflects the input of its volunteer recorders and we trust that we have done justice to the incredible efforts made by them over the past decades. We hope that they will wish to keep up the good work in future years!

Butterfly record collection

Records are collected through various means, many of which were used to collect records for the previous Upper Thames Branch atlases. Casual butterfly recording (sightings of all species seen in a location on a single date); butterfly site recording (collecting records of all species seen on different dates, from one location visited frequently); garden survey (all records during the season from single gardens); churchyard survey (collecting records from various churchyards). We also organise recording from individual 10km OS grid squares (compiled and co-ordinated by a 10km-square 'champion'). Some records are submitted using standardised paper recording forms. Increasingly, records have been submitted electronically, for example, as Excel files, exports from other systems such as MapMate, and through the on-line iRecord Butterflies App developed and hosted by the Biological Records Centre at the Centre for Ecology and Hydrology (CEH). Some records are simply emailed to the branch by casual observers.

Records from schemes administered nationally (such as the Big Butterfly Count, the iRecord Butterflies App and the national Garden Recording scheme) are fed back to us annually, we also exchange records with partner organisations, as noted in Acknowledgements.

All records from these various sources were collated and analysed using the Levana butterfly recording system, used in a number of branches of Butterfly Conservation and also to collate and analyse national records.

Together, these provide us with a basis for analysing **butterfly distributions**, which show us the geographical range of species within our region and changes in that range over time.

We participate in two standardised monitoring schemes operated at a UK scale: the Transect Recording scheme and the Wider Countryside Butterfly Scheme, both components of the United Kingdom Butterfly Monitoring Scheme (UKBMS) – a collaborative effort between Butterfly Conservation and the Centre for Ecology and Hydrology. Data collected centrally by these schemes is also fed back to us annually.

These latter two schemes provide us with data for analysis of **population trends**, which show how average population levels of species change locally, related to the density of species on monitored sites.

Information is fed back periodically to recorders on coverage of local areas, with requests to visit poorly recorded areas. In response, recorders visit particular sites or survey wider areas, for example, by walking along public footpaths, record all species they identify and make at least an estimate of the numbers of each species seen. Recorders are asked to visit sites at different points in the flight season, for example, in early-May, mid-June, mid-July and mid- to late August, covering periods of time when each of our local species is at the adult stage and also to record any immature life stages, such as eggs or larvae, that may have been seen. We aim to meet nationally-established recording standards for butterflies, which include identifying the location of records using the Ordnance Survey grid system to an accuracy of at least 1km (sometimes referred to referred to as 4-figure) and where possible identify sightings of more threatened species to 100m precision (6-figure). This allows us better to confirm and take follow-up conservation action to best manage sites associated with these species.

Moth records (including day-flying moths often seen during butterfly surveys) are collated and analysed separately (see contact details on page 71).

Data verification

With information arriving from such disparate sources, we need to carry out quality checks on the records to ensure that we can rely on them. We search for and remove duplicate records, where possible. Similarly, we verify species records, particularly for the rarer species, mainly with the help of our local 'species champions', removing those where no obvious location can be determined and those our local experts decide are unverifiable, after checking back with the recorder (e.g. records of rare species appearing in large numbers at a site not previously known for them and/or at the wrong time of year, where there is no supporting evidence).

We note that the range of different ways in which records are collected and variations in coverage across our region mean that some of our conclusions are subject to limitations inevitable with such data. We have sought to carry out analysis in ways that are not strongly affected by these limitations and we are confident that our conclusions are robust.

Data coverage and recording effort

The total recording effort achieved in the two ten-year time periods covered by this atlas is summarised in the table below, which shows the number of separate visits, the number of species records and the number of 2km squares visited during each period:

Survey period:	1995–2004	2005–2014
Number of visits	69,316	151,236
Number of species records	243,365	479,368
Number of 2km squares visited	1560	1558

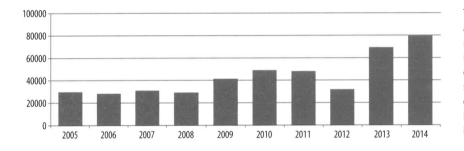

The graph here provides a summary of the total number of species records received for each of the past ten years. It shows a steady increase over the decade, and the impact of a poor summer in 2012.

The maps below show the number of visits made to each 2km square within the two ten-year survey periods. These maps indicate broadly similar levels of visit coverage across the three counties, with a tendency towards better coverage towards the central areas and also better coverage towards the south and east in the period 2005–2014.

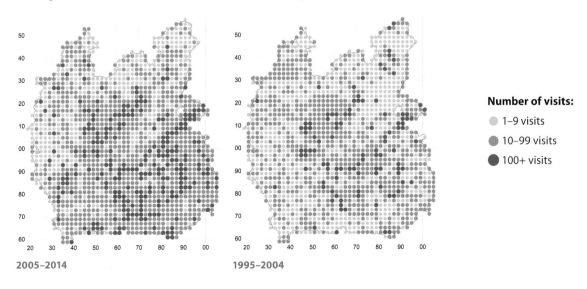

Number of visits:
- 1–9 visits
- 10–99 visits
- 100+ visits

2005–2014   1995–2004

Number of visits:

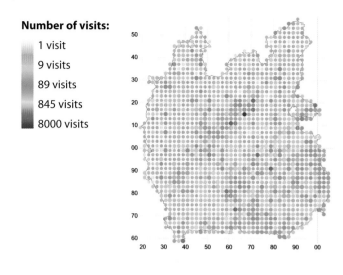

	1 visit
	9 visits
	89 visits
	845 visits
	8000 visits

Within the generally good coverage of the area, there are some 2km squares that receive much higher numbers of visits than others. This effect shows in the map here of numbers of visits shown on a logarithmic 'rainbow' colour scale. There are particularly high numbers of visits to popular sites such as Rushbeds (SP6614), Bernwood (SP6010), Finemere (SP7020) and Aston Rowant (SU7296) and to a number of sites along the Chilterns, for example.

This map also highlights the generally higher level of visits in the south-east corner and a band showing more visits in the woodland areas north-east and south-west of the centre of the map (between Oxford and Buckingham), and in an area of the Downs north of Lambourn (SU38).

The map also shows a scattering of 2km squares, especially towards the north and west of our region, that have received only a few (1–3 visits) over this ten-year period. Given the need to record at different times of year, such a small number of visits will not sample all species and these squares should be considered to be under-recorded.

Data analysis

The records were analysed to generate the maps in the species accounts section showing distribution of individual species plotted at a resolution of 2km squares aligned with the Ordnance Survey national grid. The recorded presence of species is shown using coloured dots in three categories. These depict the maximum number of butterflies seen on any one visit during the recording period, ranging from only one seen at any time, a maximum of 2–9 seen, and 10 or more seen. Where a single sighting is made on more than one visit, the dot is increased to the 2–9 category. This method of analysis is relatively unaffected by repetition of a record made by more than one observer on a given day (as occasionally happens).

Where an early stage is identified, such as an egg, larva or pupa, this is regarded as positive evidence of breeding and the relevant dot on the map is shown as at least category 2 (2–9 seen).

Note that, particularly for the more threatened species, there are some singleton records well away from the nearest established population, which it has not been possible to confirm. Whilst it is possible that some of these may be mis-identifications, we have left these in the maps, as they may represent a genuine, but small population, or they may be vagrants. The maps for Chalkhill Blue (see page 56) show an example of such singleton records.

About our region – orientation

The three counties of Berkshire, Buckinghamshire and Oxfordshire cover a range of different landscapes, extending from the intensively built-up areas in the south east (east Berkshire and south Buckinghamshire) to the relatively rural areas of the western part of the region (West Berkshire and West Oxfordshire).

The map here shows the main towns and the roads crossing our region, and should help you to orient yourself and to identify locations on the species maps.

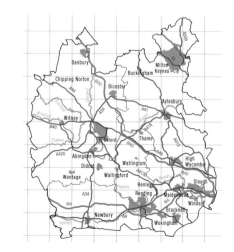

National Character Areas

English Nature has defined National Character Areas (NCAs), which are natural subdivisions of England based on a combination of landscape, biodiversity, geodiversity and economic activity (see Natural England, 2014). Each NCA is distinctive with a unique 'sense of place'. There are 159 NCAs and they follow natural, rather than administrative, boundaries. The NCA framework is used to describe and shape objectives for the countryside, its planning and management.

Twelve of these NCAs cover our region, shown in the map here, following the numbering and names assigned by Natural England.

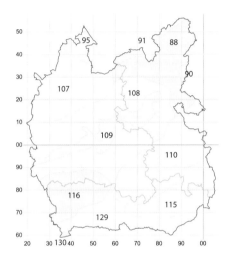

NCA	NCA Name
88	West Anglian Plain
90	Bedfordshire Greensand Ridge
91	Yardley-Whittlewood Ridge
95	Midland Clay Pastures
107	Cotswolds
108	Thames and Avon Vales
109	Midvale Ridge
110	Chilterns
115	London Basin
116	Berkshire and Marlborough Downs
129	Thames Basin Heaths
130	Hampshire Downs

The maps shown in the species section have the NCAs as background shading and show how the distributions of some species correlate with the NCAs.

So, while conservation organisations still work to maintain quality habitat within existing sites with interesting biodiversity, they also try to influence management of the land bordering those sites, especially where separate sites with high diversity of particularly threatened key species can be more closely connected.

View from Aston Rowant (Chilterns NCA), looking north-west across the Vale of Oxford (Thames and Avon Vales NCA).

SPECIES ACCOUNTS

The species accounts follow the taxonomic order of species currently recognised by Butterfly Conservation in the new checklist published by Agassiz *et al.* (2013). Note that this has changed from the earlier local atlases.

For each species, a map of records from the more recent survey period (2005–2014) is shown in full colour, alongside a map of records from the earlier survey period (1995–2004) shown partly faded, to illustrate distribution changes.

The maps are drawn on a background grid, representing the Ordnance Survey (OS) National Grid, at 10km intervals, with corresponding numbering. The post-1974 boundaries for Berkshire (lower part), Buckinghamshire (upper right) and Oxfordshire (upper left) are superimposed on the grid. This area effectively covers the current local authority areas of East and West Berkshire, Reading, Buckinghamshire, Milton Keynes and Oxfordshire. The underlying shading in the maps of the recent survey period represents the National Character Areas (see page 7).

Species records are plotted on these maps, using three symbols, as follows:
- ○ 1 individual seen on any visit.
- ◔ 2–9 seen on any one visit (or a single individual seen on at least two visits).
- ● 10 or more seen on any one visit.

Records of immature stages count as equivalent to a minimum of two adults.

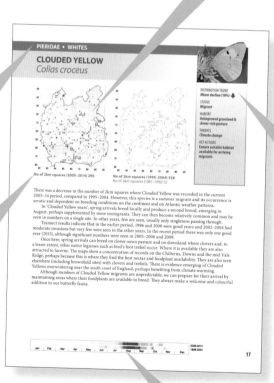

The species are grouped, with the header bar colour coded within 'families', such as the Skippers (Hesperiidae), the Whites (Pieriidae), etc.

Summary information on the number of 2km squares in which each species was recorded in each of the atlas survey periods 2005–2014 and 1995–2004, the changes between these periods, and the number for the survey period 1987–1992.

For each species, there is a photograph of the butterfly, approximately scaled according to size, with summary information on:
DISTRIBUTION TREND (local) – whether increasing, decreasing, or stable.
POPULATION TREND (local, if available) – whether increasing or decreasing.
STATUS: Conservation status, where appropriate, at National (UK) and Regional (SE England) levels.
HABITAT: as appropriate.
THREATS: to the species (if known).
KEY ACTION: needed to conserve the species locally.

Coloured strip to illustrate the flight period of each species, to provide a comparison between records from the recent survey period 2005–2014 (upper strip) and the earlier recording period 1995–2004 (lower strip). The colour range represents the total number of butterflies seen within three-day time intervals, with further smoothing applied for clarity of illustration.

DINGY SKIPPER
Erynnis tages

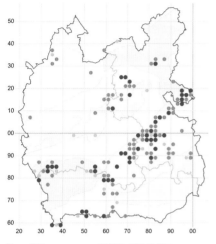

No. of 2km squares (2005–2014) 144

No. of 2km squares (1995–2004) 116
No. of 2km squares (1987–1992) 106

DISTRIBUTION TREND
Increase (24%) ⬆

POPULATION TREND
No change

STATUS
National: High priority
Local: Medium priority

HABITAT
Nutrient poor soils, especially calcareous grassland

THREATS
Habitat loss and fragmentation

KEY ACTION
Good grassland management

Dingy Skipper is, despite its name, an interesting butterfly close-up, with its richly patterned, albeit brown wings. It flies in spring with a low buzzing flight close to the ground and males are aggressive in seeing off other males within a territorial patch.

Eggs are laid on its main foodplant, common bird's-foot-trefoil. Pale yellowish in colour when newly laid, eggs turn bright orange in a few days and may be found fairly readily if you search on the foodplant leaves.

The distribution maps show that this butterfly is mainly found on the chalk grasslands of the Downs and Chilterns, and hilly areas of north-west Buckinghamshire and parts of north Oxfordshire. There has been an increase of 24% in the number of 2km squares in which it has been recorded in the recent decade, compared to 1995–2004. During the last ten years, Dingy Skipper's distribution appears to have increased along the Hampshire border and across the Chilterns. It is possible that we are still finding new local populations of this butterfly, which is easy to overlook because of its small size, moth-like appearance and early flight period.

Numbers seen vary from year to year. The national population trend for Dingy Skipper is an increase of 73% over ten years, although in our local area populations have remained relatively stable over this period.

The butterfly still depends on having good availability of its larval foodplant on sites that are kept well-grazed with good nectar sources available during late spring. If we can maintain these types of sites, this butterfly may continue to prosper.

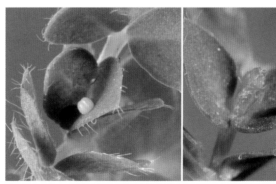

Dingy Skipper egg – pale when laid, turns orange after a few days.

Jan	Feb	Mar	Apr	May	Jun	Jul	Aug	Sep	Oct	Nov	Dec

2005-2014
1995-2004

GRIZZLED SKIPPER
Pyrgus malvae

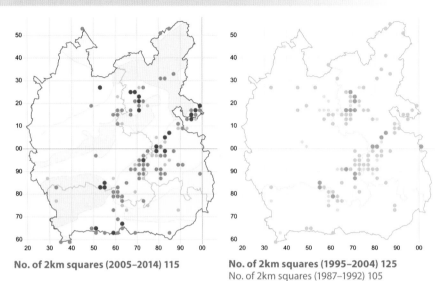

No. of 2km squares (2005–2014) 115

No. of 2km squares (1995–2004) 125
No. of 2km squares (1987–1992) 105

DISTRIBUTION TREND
Little change in population

POPULATION TREND
Slight decline

STATUS
National: High priority
Regional: Medium priority

HABITAT
Calcareous grassland,
brownfield sites and
woodland

THREATS
Habitat loss and
fragmentation

KEY ACTION
Good grassland management

Grizzled Skipper is a small butterfly with a low buzzing flight close to the ground; it is hard to spot until you recognise the flight 'jizz'. It is often found on the same sites as Dingy Skipper, and they both fly early in Spring. Eggs are laid on its foodplants of wild strawberry, agrimony and creeping cinquefoil.

The distribution maps show that Grizzled Skipper is, in common with Dingy Skipper, mainly found on the chalk grasslands of the Downs and Chilterns, and the hilly areas of NW Buckinghamshire as well as parts of north Oxfordshire. There has been a modest decrease (8%) in the number of 2km squares in which it has been recorded in the recent decade. During this period Grizzled Skipper's distribution appears to have increased along the Hampshire border but has reduced across the Chilterns and towards the north of our region. It is possible that we are still unaware of some local populations of this butterfly, which is easy to overlook because of its small size and early flight period, the peak of which appears to have moved earlier 7–10 days on average between the two ten-year recording periods, probably due to climate change.

Numbers seen vary markedly from year to year. The national population trend for Grizzled Skipper has been stable over ten years; in our area, there has also been little change in its local population trend.

The butterfly depends on having good availability of its larval foodplants on sparsely vegetated sites that are kept well-grazed but with good nectar sources available in spring and early summer. It tends also to occur on brownfield sites which comprise established, but sparse vegetation. If we can maintain these types of sites, this butterfly may continue to occur in our area. This appears to be a greater challenge for this species than for Dingy Skipper, whose distribution trend and population trend are more positive.

Jan	Feb	Mar	Apr	May	Jun	Jul	Aug	Sep	Oct	Nov	Dec

2005-2014
1995-2004

ESSEX SKIPPER
Thymelicus lineola

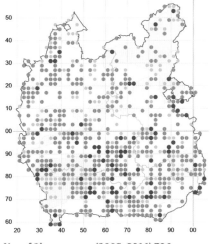

No. of 2km squares (2005–2014) 706

No. of 2km squares (1995–2004) 871
No. of 2km squares (1987–1992) 483

DISTRIBUTION TREND
Decline (19%)

POPULATION TREND
Decline (14%)

STATUS
National: Low priority
Local: Low priority

HABITAT
Dry semi-natural grassland and meadows

THREATS
Habitat loss and fragmentation

KEY ACTION
Maintain areas of rough semi-natural grassland

Essex Skipper is a fairly common butterfly in rough grassland, where it can be seen in the same places as Small Skipper, flying low as it darts amongst longer grass in dry areas. The tips of Essex Skipper antennae appear to have been dipped in black ink (see photo), distinguishing it from the otherwise similar Small Skipper, whose antennae have brown tips. It tends to prosper most where there are rough field margins, along footpaths and in open semi-natural grassland. It does also appear in gardens (15% in the 2014 garden survey) which are in reasonable proximity to wild grassy areas, where, in common with its close relative, Small Skipper, is often seen nectaring on plants such as thistles, knapweed, brambles and marjoram. It does not typically occur in agriculturally 'improved' grassland and there will be few areas of suitable habitat in highly urbanised landscapes.

The distribution of this species extended to the north and west across Oxfordshire in the early 1990s and is now found across our three counties. The general pattern has not changed much between the earlier and more recent ten-year periods. It has been recorded in about half of the 2km squares in both periods. Gaps in its coverage are likely to be partly as a result of under-recording of this small butterfly with the challenge of distinguishing it from Small Skipper, which may mask true occurrence. If suitable rough grassy areas have not been visited, it will not have been recorded.

The number of recorded 2km squares has shown a decline of 19% between the two periods, with most losses occurring in the north of the region. There has been a concurrent decline in abundance of 14% in monitored populations within the region since 1995, mirroring declines elsewhere in England.

Jan	Feb	Mar	Apr	May	Jun	Jul	Aug	Sep	Oct	Nov	Dec

2005-2014
1995-2004

SMALL SKIPPER
Thymelicus sylvestris

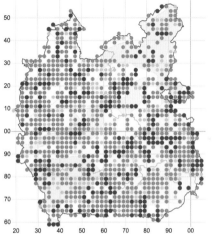

No. of 2km squares (2005–2014) 1114

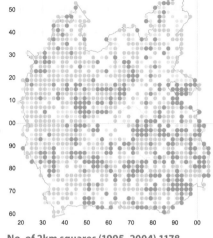

No. of 2km squares (1995–2004) 1178
No. of 2km squares (1987–1992) 1075

DISTRIBUTION TREND
Decline (5%) ⬇

POPULATION TREND
Decline (15%)

STATUS
National: Low priority
Local: Low priority

HABITAT
Rough semi-natural grassland and meadows

THREATS
Habitat loss and fragmentation, overgrazing

KEY ACTIONS
Maintain areas of rough semi-natural grassland

Small Skipper is a relatively common butterfly in rough grassland, where it can be seen flying low as it darts amongst longer grasses in dry areas, with males seeking out females, and females egg-laying in the leaf-sheath of its foodplant grasses. They are often seen nectaring on plants such as thistles, knapweed, brambles and marjoram. The brown tips of its antennae (see photo) distinguish it from its near-relative, Essex Skipper, whose antennae have clearly marked, contrasting black tips.

It occurs wherever there are rough semi-natural dry grassy areas, including rough field margins, along footpaths and in open semi-natural grassland. It appears in gardens in reasonable proximity to wild grassy areas, nectaring on smaller flowers, being seen in almost half the gardens in the 2014 UTB garden survey. However, it rarely breeds in gardens where areas of longer grass are normally too small and frequently too shady. It does not occur in agriculturally 'improved' grassland or in dense woodland and there will be few areas of suitable habitat within highly urbanised landscapes.

The distribution of this species across our three counties has not changed much. It has been recorded in over 70% of 2km squares in both periods, and gaps in its coverage are likely to be due to under-recording. Some observers find it hard to differentiate between the tiny, rapidly moving 'golden skipper' species and in areas with few suitable rough grassy areas, those supporting the species may have not been visited, so it will not have been recorded.

The local population trend from transect monitoring shows a 15% decline since 1995, mirroring the decline seen across the whole of England over this period. The number of recorded 2km squares occupied over this period has remained relatively stable however, with a decline of 5% between the two periods. Small Skipper benefited from set-aside in agriculture and similar practices should be encouraged.

The tips of Small Skipper antennae are brown.

| Jan | Feb | Mar | Apr | May | Jun | Jul | Aug | Sep | Oct | Nov | Dec |

2005-2014
1995-2004

SILVER-SPOTTED SKIPPER
Hesperia comma

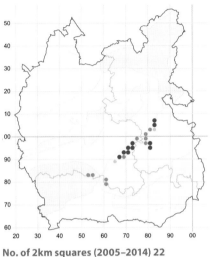

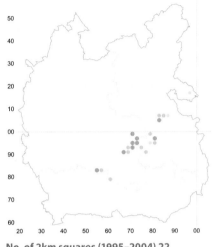

No. of 2km squares (2005–2014) 22

No. of 2km squares (1995–2004) 22
No. of 2km squares (1987–1992) 11

DISTRIBUTION TREND
Stable

STATUS
National: Medium priority
Local: Medium priority

HABITAT
Calcareous grassland

THREATS
Reduction in grazing; overgrazing and badly timed grazing; scrub invasion; habitat fragmentation

KEY ACTION
Maintain short broken turf in a connected network of warm downland sites

This warmth-loving butterfly is found in our region in a range of discrete sites along the scarp of the southern part of the Chiltern Hills; predominantly on sunny, south-facing, steep slopes with short, broken turf containing its sole larval foodplant, sheep's-fescue. Once much more widely distributed, its northernmost site in Britain now is Beacon Hill Ellesborough, near Wendover. Its strongholds in our region are on reserves at Aston Rowant and Watlington Hill.

Its distribution and abundance grew strongly from a low point in 1980 until 2000, although there have subsequently been equal numbers of gains and losses of sites in recent years, with 22 squares occupied in both atlas survey periods. Major surveys of this species in 2000 and 2009 by university researchers showed little change in the number of populations in the Chilterns network, but with several colonisations and extinctions (Lawson 2013, Davies 2006). However, since 2009, there have been no reported sightings from the Berkshire Downs or from former outlying sites at Hartslock Nature Reserve, Turville Hill, Coombe Hill and Bacombe Warren.

Silver-spotted Skipper vies with Brown Hairstreak as our last species to emerge each year, appearing in mid to late July. The large, creamy-white, domed eggs are relatively easy to find in August and September, attached to the fine blades of sheep's-fescue usually adjacent to warm, bare soil.

By 2000, it had occupied a wider range of aspects than in previous decades and was recorded laying eggs away from bare ground, although latterly this trend has reversed. Climatic warming is expected to benefit this skipper in Britain, counteracting the recent range retraction, provided that good habitat is maintained by appropriately intensive grazing in a network of inter-connected sites. However, Silver-spotted Skipper is very reluctant to disperse – researchers found no exchange of over 1200 marked individuals between the three main areas of the Aston Rowant reserve (Adey 2010) – it therefore seems unlikely to re-colonise the Berkshire Downs unaided.

Jan	Feb	Mar	Apr	May	Jun	Jul	Aug	Sep	Oct	Nov	Dec

2005-2014
1995-2004

LARGE SKIPPER
Ochlodes sylvanus

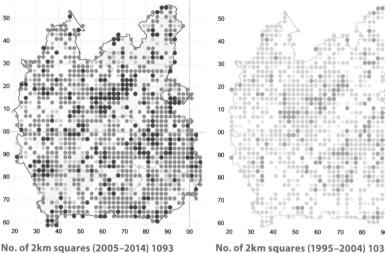

No. of 2km squares (2005–2014) 1093

No. of 2km squares (1995–2004) 1038
No. of 2km squares (1987–1992) 1038

DISTRIBUTION TREND
Minor increase (5%)

POPULATION TREND
Slight decline (2.5%)

STATUS
National: Low priority
Regional: Low priority

HABITAT
Grasslands, woodland rides, field margins and road verges

THREATS
None

KEY ACTIONS
Maintain grassy areas, where foodplants grow in sheltered, often damp, situations and remain tall and uncut

Large Skipper is widely distributed within the Upper Thames region, recorded from 1093 2km squares in the last ten years (70% of 2km squares in the region). Its range has changed little between the survey periods, although it has perhaps become more common at the southern edge of the region. Monitoring of abundance at fixed transect locations, in churchyards and garden survey reports all show a relatively stable trend, with a fall and then a recovery in numbers over the last decade. It was seen in 33% of gardens in the 2014 garden survey. This species has mottled markings on its wings, unlike the smaller Small and Essex Skippers which lack any mottling. The size and upperside markings of Large Skipper are superficially similar to those of Silver-spotted Skipper, although the latter is restricted to a few downland sites with short vegetation and, as its name suggests, has distinctive silver patches on its olive-green underwings.

Large Skipper has a single generation each year and is on the wing for the relatively extended period of mid May into August, with peak numbers in mid to late June. Colonies occur in a wide range of habitats where rough grassland persists, such as unimproved grassland, along hedgerows, road verges and within woodland rides and glades. It appears to do better in slightly damper and shadier positions, so is less frequent in the centre of large open areas. Eggs are preferentially laid on large clumps of its main foodplant, the commonly-occurring grass, cock's-foot.

Although this remains a widely-occurring species, it will continue to be locally at risk from intensification of agriculture and removal of areas of rough grassland areas perceived to be 'untidy'. Climate warming is likely to be beneficial for this species, which has been expanding northwards through Britain in recent years, although drought conditions, if they became more frequent, would be detrimental.

Jan	Feb	Mar	Apr	May	Jun	Jul	Aug	Sep	Oct	Nov	Dec

2005-2014
1995-2004

WOOD WHITE
Leptidea sinapis

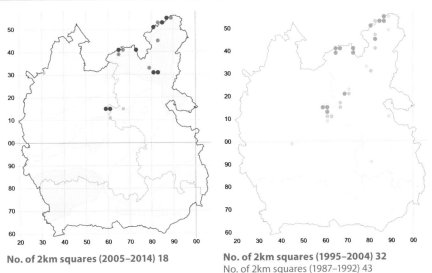

No. of 2km squares (2005–2014) 18

No. of 2km squares (1995–2004) 32
No. of 2km squares (1987–1992) 43

DISTRIBUTION TREND ⬇
Serious decline (44%)

STATUS
National: High priority
Local: High priority

HABITAT
Open Woodland margins

THREATS
Habitat fragmentation, deer browsing, change in woodland usage

KEY ACTIONS
Habitat maintenance / creation

Wood White is rapidly declining in the Upper Thames Region. Small colonies still exist in northern Buckinghamshire, but some of the featured colonies are centred within Northamptonshire, within 2km squares overlapping the border with Buckinghamshire. The last reported sighting from Whitecross Green Wood (once a stronghold) was in 2008, and the last report from Bernwood was in 1999.

The decline in Wood White population in the UK has been highlighted in many reports, which produce figures (for different time frames) of between 49% and 65%. All authorities appear agreed that the decline is mainly due to changes within our woodland habitat.

Wood White breeds in sunny woodland rides with semi-shaded ride sides. These conditions generally occur within young woodland plantations or coppiced woodland; additionally the butterfly prefers minimum cutting of marginal vegetation where the eggs are laid on a variety of vetch species. Sadly, these same plants are readily consumed by our ever increasing deer population.

In response to concern about the plight of the Wood White, Butterfly Conservation launched the National Wood White Recovery Project in 2007, with the aim of sharing information between all the stakeholders and a national sites dossier was produced (Joy, 2010). One important finding was the crucial necessity for habitats to provide their foodplants among short, warmer turf in spring and shadier turf in the summer. We feel that many former sites now fail to provide the short turf required in the spring as various factors trigger excessive early growth of various plants.

The flight period of Wood White has advanced by about two weeks between the two recording periods with a more distinct appearance of a partial second brood. This is likely to be due to climate warming.

Conservation advice describes the need to provide a large block of sheltered marginal vegetation, with plentiful vetches, growing in a range of microclimates, suitable to the needs of the butterfly in both the spring and summer broods. It is a challenge to find the resources to carry out such particular woodland management in our area on a wide enough scale.

Jan	Feb	Mar	Apr	May	Jun	Jul	Aug	Sep	Oct	Nov	Dec

2005-2014
1995-2004

ORANGE-TIP
Anthocharis cardamines

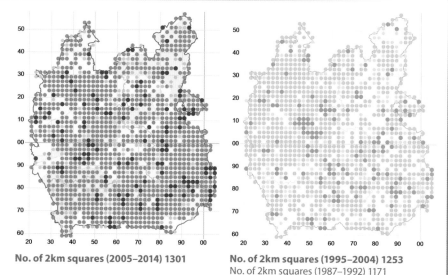

No. of 2km squares (2005–2014) 1301

No. of 2km squares (1995–2004) 1253
No. of 2km squares (1987–1992) 1171

DISTRIBUTION TREND
Minor increase (4%) ↑

POPULATION TREND
No change

STATUS
National: Low priority
Local: Low priority

HABITAT
Widespread

THREATS
None

KEY ACTIONS
Maintain suitable damp habitats

The male Orange-tip is an easily recognisable sign of spring and, although the female is less conspicuous, her orange eggs can be found throughout the countryside. The butterfly is widespread and wide-ranging throughout our region, frequenting gardens, parkland, damp meadows and shady roadside hedges. It might be slightly under-recorded within the distribution maps, because atlas recording often gathers momentum later in the season when the Orange-tip flight season is over. However, in the combined period 1995–2014, almost every 2km square in our region has a record.

The main larval foodplants are garlic mustard and lady's smock (cuckoo-flower), although occasionally other crucifers are used. Garlic mustard is commonly found on roadsides, in gardens and on field and woodland edges, and eggs can often be spotted even if the adults have not been seen. The cannibalistic green larvae, which are well camouflaged, can (less easily) be found feeding on the developing seed-pods.

The abundance of Orange-tip on transects is one of the most stable for our butterflies over recent decades. In the Upper Thames garden survey, Orange-tips were reported from the vast majority of gardens in both the 1995–2004 and the 2005–2014 survey periods. Figures for the churchyard survey showed below half of churchyards with records for 1996–2004 and around half for 2005–2014. Thus in both surveys there was, if anything, a slight increase.

The local flight season for orange-tip has advanced by about a week between the two ten-year survey periods, attributed to climate warming.

As long as damp habitats remain and weedy patches are not too enthusiastically tidied up by gardeners, farmers, churchyard managers and local authorities, Orange-tip is likely to continue to flourish in our region.

Orange-tip egg on garlic mustard.

Jan	Feb	Mar	Apr	May	Jun	Jul	Aug	Sep	Oct	Nov	Dec

2005-2014
1995-2004

LARGE WHITE
Pieris brassicae

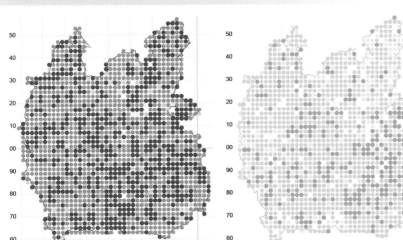

No. of 2km squares (2005–2014) 1537

No. of 2km squares (1995–2004) 1452
No. of 2km squares (1987–1993) 1508

DISTRIBUTION TREND
Minor increase (6%) ⬆

POPULATION TREND
Slight increase (2%)

STATUS
National: Low priority
Local: Low priority

HABITAT
Widespread

THREATS
None identified

KEY ACTIONS
None

Large White is a widespread and mobile butterfly, with numbers that vary dramatically through the year and from year to year. It is most frequent in years when the home-grown populations are supplemented by migrant influxes from continental Europe. It has been recorded from almost all 2km squares in our region and is a common visitor to gardens, where it is often nectars on buddleia.

The gregarious larvae are well-known pests of cultivated brassicas. Eggs are laid in large batches (typically 50–100 eggs) in neat and compact hexagonal arrays on the undersides of food plant leaves. Large numbers of adult butterflies are often seen in mid-summer over fields of oilseed rape, which clearly attracts them. Pest control measures and high levels of predation by a parasitic wasp, *Apantales glomeratus*, add further variability to butterfly numbers. Large Whites will lay also on nasturtiums in your garden, where you can later see their boldly patterned caterpillars feeding voraciously on the leaves.

Large White egg-laying on garlic mustard leaf.

Large White caterpillar on nasturtium.

Large White eggs.

Jan	Feb	Mar	Apr	May	Jun	Jul	Aug	Sep	Oct	Nov	Dec

2005-2014
1995-2004

SMALL WHITE
Pieris rapae

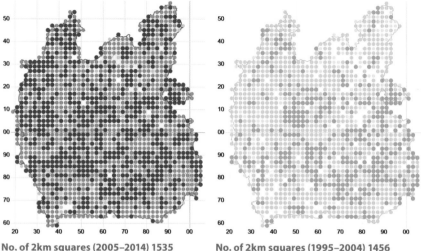

No. of 2km squares (2005–2014) 1535

No. of 2km squares (1995–2004) 1456
No. of 2km squares (1987–1992) 1480

DISTRIBUTION TREND
Minor increase (6%) ⬆

POPULATION TREND
Slight decrease (2%)

STATUS
National: Low priority
Local: Low priority

HABITAT
Widespread

THREATS
None identified

A common species in our region and a frequent visitor to gardens, Small White was recorded in 99% of 2km squares during 2005–14, 6% more 2km squares in the last decade than the preceding ten year survey period. From distribution recording and monitoring populations via transect counts, the status of this species appears to be relatively stable with year-to-year fluctuations, probably related to weather. Numbers are also boosted by the arrival of immigrants from the continent, although not to the extent seen for Large White.

In common with Large White, the larvae of Small White are known pests of cultivated brassicas and are subject to control through pesticides, which might have a larger impact in some years than others. Unlike Large White, which lays eggs in large batches, Small Whites lay eggs singly (see photo) and their uniformly green caterpillars are less apparent and less intensively destructive than those of

Small White egg.

Large White. A few Small White caterpillars are sometimes found feeding together with a larger number of large White caterpillars. In gardens, Small White tends to be seen more often nectaring on smaller flowers, such as marjoram or lavender, than on buddleia.

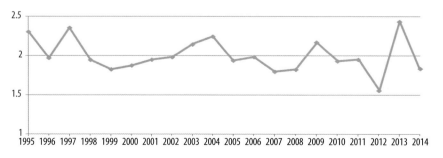

UKBMS population trend

GREEN-VEINED WHITE
Pieris napi

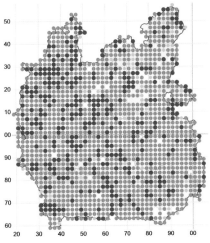

No. of 2km squares (2005–2014) 1505

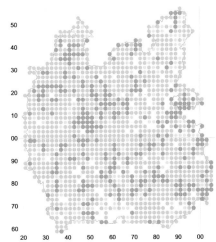

No. of 2km squares (1995–2004) 1453
No. of 2km squares (1987–1993) 1404

DISTRIBUTION TREND
Minor increase (4%) ⬆

POPULATION TREND
No change

STATUS
National: Low priority
Local: Low priority

HABITAT
Widespread

THREATS
No major threat, but loss of 'edge' habitat could become a concern

Green-veined White was recorded in over 90% of 2km squares in all survey periods, although 2012 was a notably poor year for this species. There was a slight increase in the number of squares recorded in the last ten year period with some infilling within its geographic range. Population numbers from transect monitoring were relatively stable over the last 20 years.

The data indicate that, between the two ten-year survey periods, the flight period of this species may have extended by a few days at the start and end of the season.

Green-veined White.

Compared with its near relatives, this species rarely selects cultivated plants for egg-laying and should be less harmed by pesticides; and there is no evidence for directed parasitoid attack by species that specialise in finding the larvae (as there is for Large White *P. brassicae*). However, its greater dependence on wild cruciferae species, growing along woodland edges, in hedges, within scrub and other damp, lightly vegetated habitats, may place this butterfly at greater risk than its near relatives from attempts to 'tidy-up' the landscape. Thus, efforts to encourage conservation of these habitats should be maintained. If climate change produces drier summers this may adversely affect its larval foodplants and therefore this butterfly.

Jan	Feb	Mar	Apr	May	Jun	Jul	Aug	Sep	Oct	Nov	Dec

2005-2014
1995-2004

CLOUDED YELLOW
Colias croceus

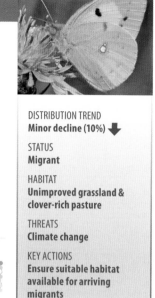

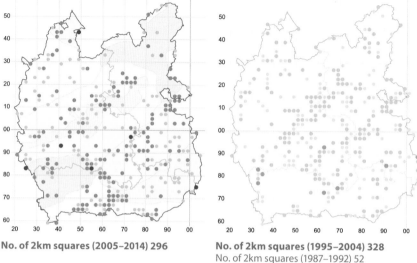

No. of 2km squares (2005–2014) 296

No. of 2km squares (1995–2004) 328
No. of 2km squares (1987–1992) 52

DISTRIBUTION TREND
Minor decline (10%) ⬇

STATUS
Migrant

HABITAT
Unimproved grassland & clover-rich pasture

THREATS
Climate change

KEY ACTIONS
Ensure suitable habitat available for arriving migrants

There was a decrease in the number of 2km squares where Clouded Yellow was recorded in the current 2005–14 period, compared to 1995–2004. However, this species is a summer migrant and its occurrence is erratic and dependent on breeding conditions on the continent and on Atlantic weather patterns.

In 'Clouded Yellow years', spring arrivals breed locally and produce a second brood, emerging in August, perhaps supplemented by more immigrants. They can then become relatively common and may be seen in numbers on a single site. In other years, few are seen, usually only singletons passing through.

Transect results indicate that in the earlier period, 1996 and 2000 were good years and 2002–2004 had moderate invasions but very few were seen in the other years. In the recent period there was only one good year (2013), although significant numbers were seen in 2005, 2006 and 2009.

Once here, spring arrivals can breed on clover-sown pasture and on downland where clovers and, to a lesser extent, other native legumes such as bird's-foot-trefoil occur. Where it is available they are also attracted to lucerne. The maps show a concentration of records on the Chilterns, Downs and the mid-Vale Ridge, perhaps because this is where they find the best nectar and foodplant availability. They are also seen elsewhere (including brownfield sites) with clovers and trefoils. There is evidence emerging of Clouded Yellows overwintering near the south coast of England, perhaps benefiting from climate warming.

Although numbers of Clouded Yellow migrants are unpredictable, we can prepare for their arrival by maintaining areas where their foodplants are available to breed. They always make a welcome and colourful addition to our butterfly fauna.

Jan	Feb	Mar	Apr	May	Jun	Jul	Aug	Sep	Oct	Nov	Dec

2005-2014
1995-2004

BRIMSTONE
Gonepteryx rhamni

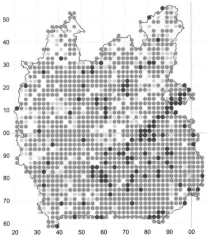

No. of 2km squares (2005–2014) 1350

No. of 2km squares (1995–2004) 1217
No. of 2km squares (1987–1993) 1031

DISTRIBUTION TREND
Increase (11%) ↑

POPULATION TREND
No change

STATUS
National: Low priority
Local: Low priority

HABITAT
Widespread

THREATS
None identified

KEY ACTIONS
Encourage planting of buckthorns

Brimstone is common and widespread in our three counties (and across southern England). Our 1995–2000 survey indicated an increase in north Oxfordshire and a decrease in Berkshire, with an overall gain of 12% since 1987–92. The most recent survey period shows a further 11% increase in recorded 2km squares since 1995–2004. It also shows that any possible reduction in Berkshire was temporary as the county is now solidly occupied. Further, we believe that this highly mobile species has fewer gaps in north Oxfordshire and north Buckinghamshire than the maps show. Despite Brimstone being a readily detected species, these gaps are more likely to be due to a combination of the species flying in relatively small numbers and fewer observers reporting from those areas.

Brimstone has only one brood a year and, unusually, spends most of that year as an adult, over-wintering in hibernation from late August (after emerging in July) until March. Consequently, a suitable hibernation site is vital. Thick ivy and bramble bushes are frequently used, so Brimstones may be put at risk by gardeners 'tidying up' in winter.

Female Brimstones leave hibernation and mate in the spring of the year after they emerge. They lay eggs on the leaves of buckthorns (alder buckthorn and purging buckthorn). These eggs produce a mid-summer brood and in most years Brimstones seem to be almost continuously on the wing. A key habitat requirement is therefore buckthorn bushes situated in sunny positions, within scrub or in a hedgerow.

The future of this butterfly can be enhanced by promoting the planting of buckthorns, as ideal hedgerow plants in rural and suburban settings. Buckthorn in a garden will often be used by visiting females and their sheltered nature may make gardens a preferred habitat. The retention of ivy and bramble for use as winter hibernation sites should be encouraged.

Jan	Feb	Mar	Apr	May	Jun	Jul	Aug	Sep	Oct	Nov	Dec	2005-2014
												1995-2004

WALL
Lasiommata megera

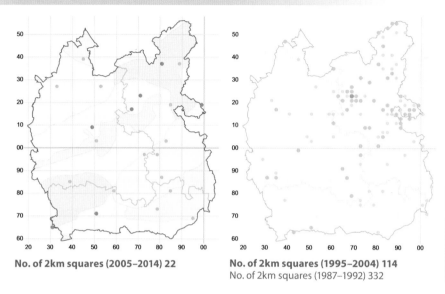

No. of 2km squares (2005–2014) 22

No. of 2km squares (1995–2004) 114
No. of 2km squares (1987–1992) 332

DISTRIBUTION TREND
Severe decline (81%) ⬇

STATUS
National: High priority
Local: High priority

HABITAT
Downland, brownfield sites,
unfertilised pasture

THREATS
Development or enrichment
of marginal land

KEY ACTIONS
Further research and
continued monitoring

The decline of Wall reported in the 2005 UK assessment 'State of Butterflies' has continued, with a drastic decrease of over 80% in the Upper Thames region, the greatest decrease of any of our local butterflies. There were only a handful of multiple records in the recent period, mostly in the north-east of our region where the majority of colonies had survived previously. Outside the former core area most recent records are of single sightings and each from unique sites, suggesting that they could have been wanderers. This species, along with the Marsh Fritillary, is currently the least likely to be found in the three counties.

Once widespread in our area, Wall probably occurred in every 10km square as recently as the early 1980s (Steel, 1985), although not always in large numbers. It prefers dry areas with short grass, such as is typical on downland, waste areas and brownfield sites; at one time the Wall could even be found in suitable gardens.

This decrease is both a UK and north-western European phenomenon. Wall has been lost from most inland areas of Southern England, although it survives in coastal areas. The butterfly has also decreased in Ireland, Spain and the Netherlands over both periods and in France since at least 2005. Although research is currently being carried out, the factors causing decline are still not certain, climate change and/or atmospheric NO_x levels being possibilities (Palmer, 2015; Van Dyck, 2015; Klop 2015). The population has fluctuated in the past and has been severely affected by a series of bad summers but other factors are highly likely to be at work, perhaps agricultural intensification and commercial development.

As we do not know the causes of the loss of this butterfly, we should continue monitoring and implement any conservation management recommendations emerging from ongoing research.

Jan	Feb	Mar	Apr	May	Jun	Jul	Aug	Sep	Oct	Nov	Dec

2005-2014
1995-2004

SPECKLED WOOD
Pararge aegeria

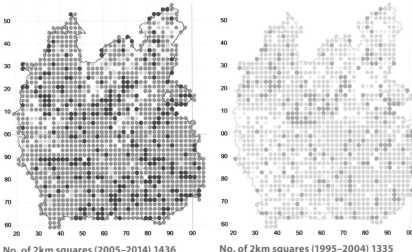

No. of 2km squares (2005–2014) 1436

No. of 2km squares (1995–2004) 1335
No. of 2km squares (1987–1992) 1251

DISTRIBUTION TREND
Increase (8%) ⬆

POPULATION TREND
Slight increase (1%)

STATUS
National: Low priority
Local: Low priority

HABITAT
Woodland, gardens,
hedgerows

THREATS
None

KEY ACTIONS
Maintain some long grass in
woods and hedgerows

Speckled Wood butterflies are common throughout the Upper Thames region. They are to be found in areas of dappled sun and shade in woodland rides and clearings, along hedgerows and in gardens. The caterpillars need areas of longer grass to feed. Speckled Woods can over-winter either as caterpillars or as pupae. With staggered emergence the following spring and two or three overlapping generations, they can potentially be seen any time between March and October.

In the 1995–2004 atlas period, Speckled Woods were recorded from almost all 2km squares, with the biggest gaps in north-east Buckinghamshire and the far west of Berkshire and Oxfordshire. In the 2005–2014 atlas period, most of the gaps had been filled, but those remaining were still concentrated in the north-east of the region.

Speckled Woods are widely reported by members in the Upper Thames survey, being recorded from between 60% and 80% of gardens. They are less commonly seen in churchyards, being reported from between 14% and 72% of the surveyed sites. Both the garden and churchyard surveys show variations from year to year, with good agreement between the peaks and troughs. 2001 and 2012 were poor years in both series, while 2009 and 2014 were both good years for Speckled Wood.

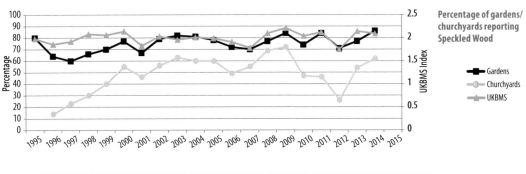

Percentage of gardens/
churchyards reporting
Speckled Wood

Gardens
Churchyards
UKBMS

2005-2014
1995-2004

SMALL HEATH
Coenonympha pamphilus

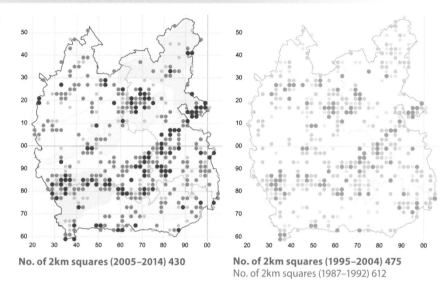

No. of 2km squares (2005–2014) 430

No. of 2km squares (1995–2004) 475
No. of 2km squares (1987–1992) 612

DISTRIBUTION TREND
Decline (9%) ⬇

POPULATION TREND
Slight increase (1%)

STATUS
National: High priority
Local: Medium priority

HABITAT
Grassland with close-cropped areas, especially chalk downland

THREATS
Soil enrichment, development of 'waste' areas

KEY ACTIONS
Maintenance of suitable habitat

The number of squares occupied by Small Heath shows a decline in the Upper Thames region of 9% between the two recording periods. An analysis of transects in the region, shown in the graph here, indicates no significant trend in populations over the second period, although the 20-year transect record from Aston Upthorpe Downs suggests an overall upwards trend. The transect data does, however, indicate a population fluctuating on a 5–7-year cycle.

While populations may appear to be relatively stable on managed sites, there are concerns at a national scale about its relatively patchy distribution in the wider countryside leading to risks of increasing local extinction as sites become unsuitable and remaining populations become more isolated.

Where it does occur, the butterfly is usually seen flying over short grass with longer grass in the vicinity, often along well-worn tracks across more extensive grassy areas. These can be found extensively on the Downs and Chilterns and also on brownfield and 'waste' sites, such as worked-out sand pits, which often have flourishing populations. Destruction of these sites due to development, for example, will threaten this species, as would changes in farming practices such as cultivation of marginal land and ploughing-up or fertilisation of permanent pasture. A priority is to manage appropriately these sites which do not have formal protection, whilst continuing to provide suitable conditions within nature reserves. We need to keep a watch on the fortunes of this butterfly in the future.

UKBMS population trend

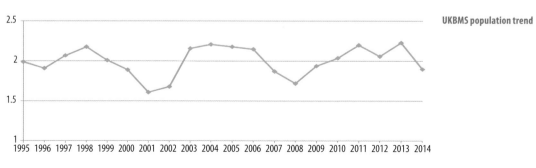

2005-2014
1995-2004

RINGLET
Aphantopus hyperantus

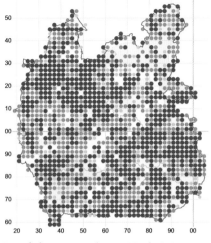

No. of 2km squares (2005–2014) 1363

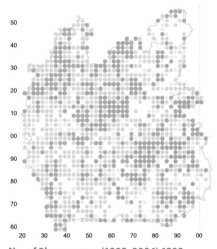

No. of 2km squares (1995–2004) 1235
No. of 2km squares (1987–1992) 1098

DISTRIBUTION TREND
Increase (11%) ⬆

POPULATION TREND
Slight increase (2%)

STATUS
National: Low priority
Local: Low priority

HABITAT
Damp rough grassland

THREATS
Drought, loss of rough grassland

KEY ACTIONS
Maintain rough grassland areas

The recovery of Ringlet from its population crash in the 1970s, noted in the last Atlas, has continued. Like the Meadow Brown, it is common and widespread, favouring areas of longer grass. However, it prefers damper habitats such as woodland rides and edges, shaded hedgerows and abandoned rough corners, so is less likely to be found in habitats such as gardens. The increase in occupied squares in farmland areas in the second atlas recording period may be an indication that Ringlets have benefited from the uncultivated field margins associated with countryside stewardship schemes.

Local transect results show an increasing population trend over both periods, with the 1996 index the lowest and that for 2014 the second highest of the two recording periods. This species is likely to suffer in drought conditions and may be benefiting from a number of recent wet summers.

Annual fluctuations in populations can be considerable and are likely to be mainly due to weather conditions. Although Ringlet appears to be not threatened at present, excessive 'tidying up' of waste ground and brownfield sites within suburban areas will reduce the area of suitable habitat for this and many other butterflies. Similarly, uncultivated field margins are important to Ringlet and other species and are susceptible to changes in management under agri-environment schemes such as Countryside Stewardship and reforms in the EU Common Agricultural Policy.

Unusual Ringlet aberration, *ab. lanceolata.*

Jan	Feb	Mar	Apr	May	Jun	Jul	Aug	Sep	Oct	Nov	Dec

2005-2014
1995-2004

MEADOW BROWN
Maniola jurtina

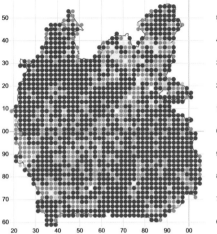

No. of 2km squares (2005–2014) 1526

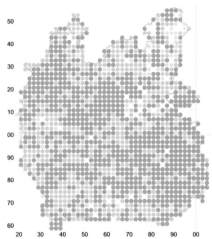

No. of 2km squares (1995–2004) 1508
No. of 2km squares (1987–1992) 1488

DISTRIBUTION TREND
Minor increase (1%) ⬆

POPULATION TREND
No change

STATUS
National: Low priority
Local: Low priority

HABITAT
Grassland

THREATS
Loss of flower-rich permanent grassland

KEY ACTIONS
Continue monitoring

Meadow Brown is one of our most widely distributed butterflies, recorded in over 97% of squares in both periods. As its caterpillar feeds on a wide range of grasses, it is likely to be found in any sizeable patch of long grass. It is also often the most abundant species when monitored on transects, with numbers being relatively stable over the last 20 years. Any variation in numbers from year to year is most likely to be the result of weather conditions.

The flight period of Meadow Brown, extending from early June through to later September, is much longer than for Gatekeeper or Ringlet. The flight chart below indicates that the flight period was starting a few days earlier and finishing a few days later in 2005–14 than in 1995–2004.

The caterpillars crawl up grass leaves to start feeding each evening, and can be found if you search among the grass leaves with a torch at dusk in late April/early May.

This familiar butterfly continues to be common in our area; nevertheless it should continue to be monitored.

Meadow Brown caterpillar.

UKBMS population trend

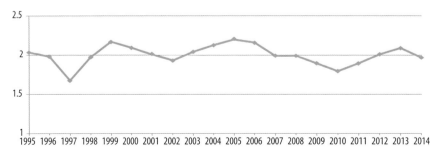

2005-2014
1995-2004

GATEKEEPER
Pyronia tithonus

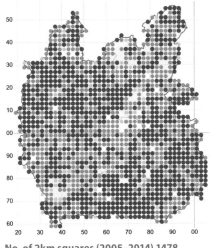

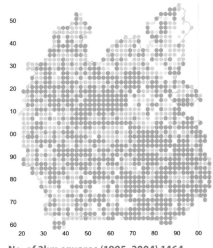

No. of 2km squares (2005–2014) 1478

No. of 2km squares (1995–2004) 1464
No. of 2km squares (1987–1992) 1379

DISTRIBUTION TREND
Minor increase (1%)

POPULATION TREND
Minor increase (3%)

STATUS
National: Low priority
Local: Low priority

HABITAT
Grassland and hedgerows

THREATS
Loss of rough grassland, scrub and hedgerows

KEY ACTIONS
Continue monitoring

Gatekeeper is one of our widespread and common 'browns', occurring in well over 94% of 2km squares in both recording periods and in over 80% of gardens. It can be the commonest butterfly during its short flight period in July and August. Transect data show a slight downward trend (-3) over the last 20 years.

Long grass is the favoured habitat, although Gatekeeper needs warmer conditions near shrubs – hence, the alternative name of 'Hedge Brown'. Loss of hedgerows and unmanaged grassland becoming dominated by scrub, pose threats to this species, which needs open grassland with some shrub growth. Gatekeepers seem to favour bramble bushes where they are often found nectaring on their flowers. This species is likely to benefit from environmental management of field margins, where longer grasses with nectar sources are allowed to grow near to walls and hedgerows.

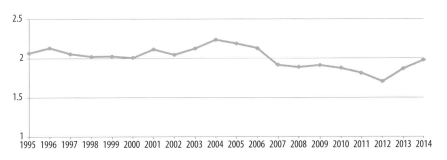

UKBMS population trend

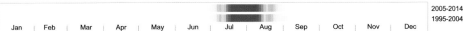

2005-2014
1995-2004

MARBLED WHITE
Melanargia galathea

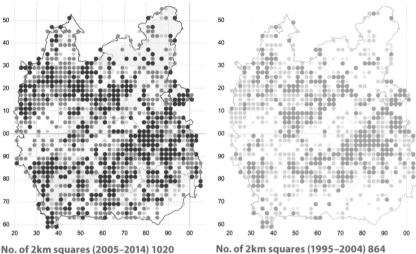

No. of 2km squares (2005–2014) 1020

No. of 2km squares (1995–2004) 864
No. of 2km squares (1987–1992) 595

DISTRIBUTION TREND
Increase (18%)

POPULATION TREND
Minor increase (2%)

STATUS
National: Low priority
Local: Low priority

HABITAT
Flower-rich medium-long grassland, field margins

THREATS
Overgrazing, scrub invasion

KEY ACTIONS
Reduce mowing of verges

Marbled White is a butterfly of flower-rich grassland with medium to long turf height. It is on the wing between June and July, and is mobile and able to colonise relatively small areas of new habitat, such as road verges and field margins. Nationally, its range is expanding to the north and the east from its heartlands in southern England. In the first atlas period, Marbled White was present in much of the Upper Thames area, but there were notable gaps in much of central and east Berkshire, north-east Buckinghamshire, the Oxford Clay area of west Oxfordshire and the stiff Gault clays around Thame and the Vale of Aylesbury. In the second atlas period, Marbled Whites were recorded from most of Berkshire, with just the acid heathlands south of Reading on the Bagshot Beds and the urban conurbations in the far east of the county remaining unsuitable. Field margins which have been left uncultivated by countryside stewardship schemes may have contributed to the increase in its range. Coverage also appears to have increased in north Oxfordshire. The biggest gaps in the latest atlas period remain in north-east Buckinghamshire, around Thame and the Vale of Aylesbury and in parts of west Oxfordshire.

Garden records show a 14% increase in the 2005–2014 period compared with the 1995–2004 period, roughly in line with the atlas data. There were peaks in 2003 and 2006, years with particularly sunny summer weather. Future changes to the management of field margins through agri-environment schemes suggest the continued need for working with landowners to promote retention of uncultivated margins.

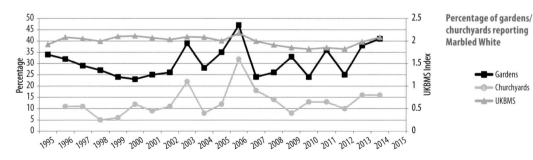

Percentage of gardens/ churchyards reporting Marbled White

- Gardens
- Churchyards
- UKBMS

2005-2014
1995-2004

| Jan | Feb | Mar | Apr | May | Jun | Jul | Aug | Sep | Oct | Nov | Dec |

GRAYLING
Hipparchia semele

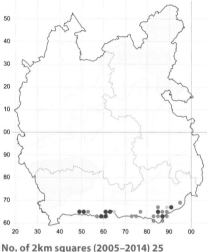

No. of 2km squares (2005–2014) 25

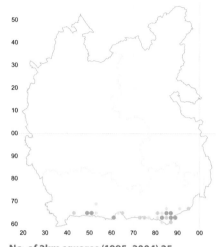

No. of 2km squares (1995–2004) 25
No. of 2km squares (1987–1992) 21

DISTRIBUTION TREND
No change

STATUS
**National: High priority
Local: Medium priority**

HABITAT
Heathland

THREATS
Soil enrichment, scrub encroachment

KEY ACTIONS
Conserve remaining heathland

Grayling is found on dry heathland habitats in southern Berkshire, near the Hampshire and Surrey borders. Occupying similar habitat to Silver-studded Blue, Grayling has less exacting requirements, persisting on sites with sufficient bare ground. Despite the loss of the last downland colony during the earliest survey period there has been a slight increase (to 25 2km squares) since then, presumably down to increased efforts to locate populations and through improved management of the remaining heathland fragments. Over the last 20 years, the number of colonies has remained static with similar numbers of individuals recorded away from known colonies in both recent surveys. These 'wanderers' give hope that, should areas of heathland be extended, the butterfly will colonise them.

The loss of extensive grazing is thought to have caused the longer term decline and now active conservation work is required to maintain suitable conditions, i.e. bare and stony ground with a sparse covering of grasses at mixed heights. This is sometimes achieved by controlled burning, carefully restricted to limited parts of heathland sites. More often though, site management is through manual labour, controlling scrub incursion with hand tools. Uncontrolled burning, by accident or vandalism, may be disastrous, leading to total loss of many species from a site, and should any site be too isolated, natural re-colonisation is unlikely.

Heathland is at risk from several threats. There is strong pressure for housing development and various remaining sites are adjacent to housing with pressure from frequent visitors. Perhaps more detrimental is the rapid succession of heathlands towards woodland, making them too shady for the species' survival. Fortunately, heathlands are increasingly taken under conservation management. Multi-partner conservation initiatives, involving Butterfly Conservation and extending into Hampshire and Surrey, are helping maintain a future for our local Grayling populations against these threats; the situation remains precarious and requires constant vigilance and action.

| Jan | Feb | Mar | Apr | May | Jun | Jul | Aug | Sep | Oct | Nov | Dec |

2005-2014
1995-2004

SILVER-WASHED FRITILLARY
Argynnis paphia

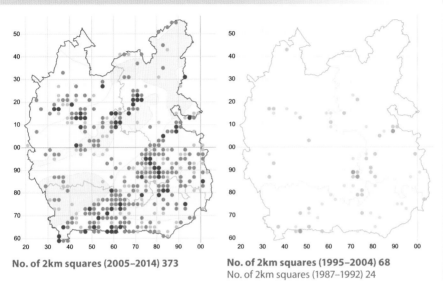

No. of 2km squares (2005–2014) 373

No. of 2km squares (1995–2004) 68
No. of 2km squares (1987–1992) 24

DISTRIBUTION TREND
Major increase (449%) ⬆

POPULATION TREND
Substantial increase (47%)

STATUS
National: Low priority
Local: Low priority

HABITAT
Broadleaved woodland with sunny rides and glades

THREATS
Habitat fragmentation, loss of clearings, browsing by deer

KEY ACTIONS
Open rides, create glades, control deer population

Silver-washed Fritillary has shown the biggest distribution increase in occupied squares between the two recording periods – over five-fold. It had been confined to a few sites along the Hampshire border in west Berkshire, a few larger Chiltern woods, including BBOWT's Warburg reserve, Wendover and Crowsley Woods, isolated populations in Windsor, Wychwood and Bernwood Forests, Wytham Woods and a few other scattered sites.

From around 2005, the number of sites began to increase dramatically. Initially, this expansion was in the Pang Valley, eastwards along the Hampshire border, outwards from the Chilterns hotspots and in the Bernwood complex of the Oxford Clay vale. Newly colonised populations continue to increase in size and the butterfly continues to expand its range. By the end of 2014, it had been recorded from most of the wooded 2km squares in Berkshire and the Chilterns, with increased populations in NW Oxfordshire and the clay vale woodlands. New sites have appeared in west Oxfordshire and north Buckinghamshire.

Silver-washed Fritillaries thrive in broad-leaved woodland with sunny clearings, open rides and abundant nectar sources, such as bramble. They are increasingly recorded in conifer plantations, if they have open flowery rides and the caterpillar foodplant, common dog-violet, is available.

Garden survey data reinforces the wider picture. From the hot summer of 2006, Silver-washed Fritillary has turned up in gardens with increasing frequency, with notable peaks in 2010, 2013 and 2014.

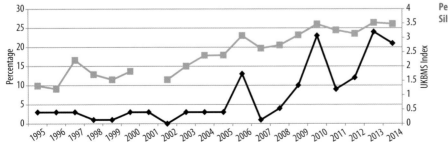

Percentage of gardens reporting
Silver-washed Fritillary

—◆— Gardens
—■— UKBMS

2005-2014
1995-2004

| Jan | Feb | Mar | Apr | May | Jun | Jul | Aug | Sep | Oct | Nov | Dec |

DARK GREEN FRITILLARY
Argynnis aglaja

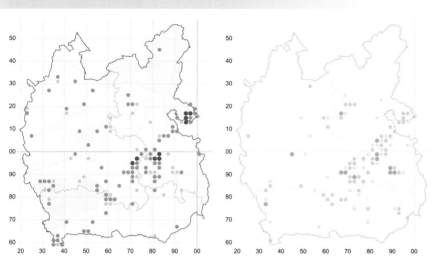

No. of 2km squares (2005–2014) 126

No. of 2km squares (1995–2004) 103
No. of 2km squares (1987–1992) 85

DISTRIBUTION TREND
Increase (22%) ⬆

POPULATION TREND
Decline (10%)

STATUS
National: Low priority
Local: Medium priority

HABITAT
Calcareous grassland

THREATS
Scrub invasion, over grazing and scrub clearance

KEY ACTIONS
Maintain a mosaic of some scrub in otherwise open areas

In our region, Dark Green Fritillary occurs predominantly on calcareous grassland. Its preferred habitat is flower-rich grassland with open scrub which is not heavily grazed. Its core areas are slopes of the Chilterns and Berkshire Downs, where the caterpillar foodplant is hairy violet. Away from the chalk, it is occasionally seen in rough pasture and woodland rides, with common dog-violet as the alternative foodplant.

The 22% increase in number of 2km squares in which Dark Green Fritillary was recorded between 1995–2004 and 2005–2014, masks a 31% decline during 2005–2009 to a low point of 68 2km squares, mirrored in transect counts. Since 2009, the number of colonies and transect population counts have steadily increased. The summer of 2013 saw a large increase in population size at several sites, such as Buttlers Hangings and Bradenham in south Buckinghamshire, where numbers increased tenfold.

Reports of scattered individuals have increased in recent years, but once sizeable colonies such as Gomm Valley in High Wycombe remain restricted to occasional singletons. Holtspur Bank, next to our reserve at Holtspur Bottom no longer supports the butterfly, perhaps because the scrub became too dense. They occur in small numbers regularly at many Chiltern and downland sites and one or two woodland sites in NW Buckinghamshire, but only Ivinghoe Beacon and Bradenham currently hold significant populations. In the period 2005–2014, there was an increase in occupied sites in NW Oxfordshire and the far south-west of Berkshire.

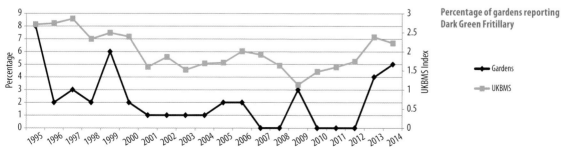

Percentage of gardens reporting Dark Green Fritillary

◆ Gardens
▪ UKBMS

2005-2014
1995-2004

WHITE ADMIRAL
Limenitis camilla

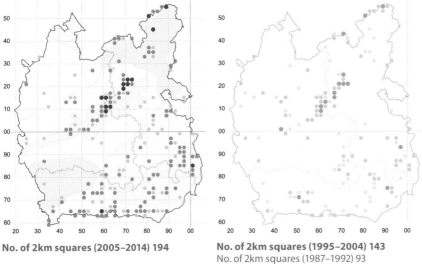

No. of 2km squares (2005–2014) 194

No. of 2km squares (1995–2004) 143
No. of 2km squares (1987–1992) 93

DISTRIBUTION TREND
Increase (36%) ↑

POPULATION TREND
Decline (4%)

STATUS
National: High priority
Local: Low priority

HABITAT
Open Woodland

THREATS
Habitat loss

The White Admiral distribution is increasing in our three counties, with a 36% increase in range since 1995–2004 and 107% increase since 1987–92. In our area, this butterfly occurs mainly in woods south of the Downs and Chilterns, and between Oxford and Buckingham. Black Park, Waterperry Wood, Bernwood Forest and Finemere Wood are among the sites where good numbers can be found.

This shade-tolerant butterfly is found in relatively mature deciduous woodland and feeds mainly on bramble flowers. Straggly growths of honeysuckle, in shaded or semi-shaded positions near rides, clearings and sheltered woodland edges, are used for egg-laying and larval feeding. Typically, it is found in later stages of woodland succession. Transects in ancient woodland typically report higher numbers than other woodland types.

The flight period of White Admiral appears to have moved a few days earlier between the two survey periods, perhaps in response to climate warming.

White Admiral has spread rapidly in England since the 1920s and continued to spread into the 1980s and 1990s, but lately, within its range, populations have declined. The earlier population increase is thought to have been caused by the decline in coppice management in the late 19th century, resulting in increases in the shadier conditions preferred by this species. During the 1930s and 1940s a series of warm summers and the neglected coppice woodland provided the ideal conditions for expansion in both population density and range. As the coppice woodlands matured or were cleared, the butterfly was lost from many sites, but the extended range has been maintained (Pollard 1981). If we can maintain suitable woodland conditions by appropriate management, we may hope to continue to see the graceful, gliding flight of this handsome butterfly in our woods for many years to come.

Jan	Feb	Mar	Apr	May	Jun	Jul	Aug	Sep	Oct	Nov	Dec

2005-2014
1995-2004

PURPLE EMPEROR
Apatura iris

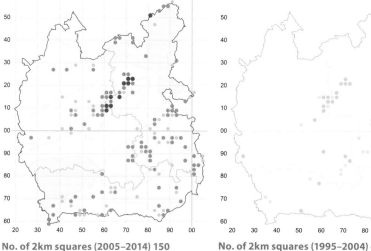

No. of 2km squares (2005–2014) 150

No. of 2km squares (1995–2004) 45
No. of 2km squares (1987–1992) 19

DISTRIBUTION TREND
Major increase (234%)

STATUS
National: Medium priority
Local: Medium priority

HABITAT
Found in large blocks of broadleaved woodland or clusters of smaller woods and/or dense scrub with a good supply of willow

THREATS
Ride clearance removing willows which tend to grow along wood edge

KEY ACTIONS
Promote retention of ride-side willow

Between the two ten-year recording periods, Purple Emperor has markedly increased its range across our region, more than doubling the number of occupied 2km squares. Expansions have occurred in all regions that were occupied at the turn of the millennium. The stronghold within our region is centred on conifer plantations and deciduous woodlands of the Bernwood Forest complex. Increases in numbers have occurred at existing locations as well as new colonies being established nearby. New colonies have been recorded in areas bordering Northamptonshire, for example, at Yardley Chase and Salcey Forest and we now find the species thinly but widely spread through the south of Berkshire. This butterfly seems far more mobile than previously thought, and able to move large distances between woods.

This magnificent butterfly is one of the most emblematic species occurring in our region. Its size and colouration, combined with an elusive nature, make it a prized species to seek out. A woodland species, Purple Emperor is often faithful to a group of three or more trees situated near hilltops where males gather to engage in competitive displays to entice visiting females. Males can also be found at ground level, seeking out vital nutrients from mud, dung or rotting flesh. Purple Emperor enthusiasts tempt individuals to descend from tree-tops to feed on strange concoctions such as shrimp paste and pungent cheese.

Conservation in woodland centres on the preservation of ride side willow species, foodplants which are under threat of clearance as part of occasional ride widening.

Trying to tempt the Emperor down with a noxious mixture.

| Jan | Feb | Mar | Apr | May | Jun | Jul | Aug | Sep | Oct | Nov | Dec |

2005-2014
1995-2004

RED ADMIRAL
Vanessa atalanta

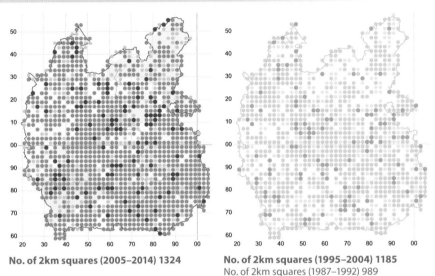

No. of 2km squares (2005–2014) 1324

No. of 2km squares (1995–2004) 1185
No. of 2km squares (1987–1992) 989

DISTRIBUTION TREND
Increase (12%) ⬆

POPULATION TREND
Slight decrease (3%)

STATUS
National: Low priority
Local: Low priority

HABITAT
Wide-ranging

THREATS
None

KEY ACTIONS
Maintain nectar resources in gardens and the countryside

Red Admiral is a widespread species and has been seen in most months of the year. Numbers of Red Admirals reaching Britain each year fluctuate greatly, mostly dependent on breeding success further south. There has been a 12% increase in recorded squares in our region since 1995–2004 and a slightly downward population trend. This butterfly now overwinters in southern England, providing a native breeding stock and sightings all year round.

Red Admiral is conspicuous in gardens on buddleia, a favourite nectar source, and on rotting fruit. As temperatures fall in late summer or autumn, adults begin flying south to Europe, with a small proportion remaining in the UK. Like other Vanessid species, Red Admiral lays its eggs on common nettle, with other plants (such as pellitory-of-the-wall) only occasionally used. Eggs are laid singly on the upper surface of a tender leaf and the resulting caterpillar develops inside a neat tent created by spinning the outer edges of the leaf together with fine silk. The distinctive chrysalis can be found in late summer, suspended within a shelter of two or three large nettle leaves.

Red Admiral pupa.

UKBMS population trend

2005-2014
1995-2004

| Jan | Feb | Mar | Apr | May | Jun | Jul | Aug | Sep | Oct | Nov | Dec |

PAINTED LADY
Vanessa cardui

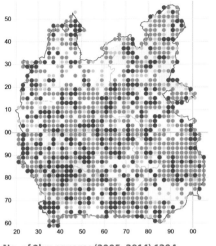

No. of 2km squares (2005–2014) 1204

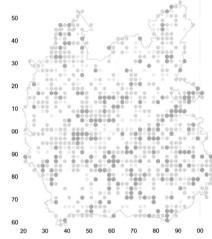

No. of 2km squares (1995–2004) 836
No. of 2km squares (1987–1992) 522

DISTRIBUTION TREND
Increase (44%) ⬆

POPULATION TREND
Decrease (7%)

STATUS
National: Low priority
Local: Low priority

HABITAT
Wide-ranging

THREATS
None known

KEY ACTIONS
None

Although Painted Lady can be common in gardens, numbers vary widely each year, depending on the strength of annual migration from North Africa via southern Europe. We recorded massive influxes in 1996 and 2009. Numbers one year show no correlation with previous year's numbers, as butterflies emerging here in late summer leave again, returning south for the winter.

In big migration years, large numbers of Painted Ladies can be seen flying strongly (at about 15mph) northwards, stopping only rarely to refuel on flowers. Confirmation that Painted Ladies return to the continent in large numbers has only recently been confirmed with the use of upward-facing radar (Stefanescu 2013).

It is a common garden butterfly, but numbers vary widely from year to year, depending on the strength of the annual migration. The percentage of gardens reporting Painted Lady in the last ten years varied from only 24% in 2012 to a massive 100% in 2009. Similar variations were seen in churchyards, with 56% in 2009 but none at all in 2011 and reflected in counts on butterfly transects.

Painted Lady larvae.

Schools breed Painted Ladies from captive livestock to teach children about the butterfly life cycle. Although typically released in spring, they do not appear to affect the annual numbers greatly.

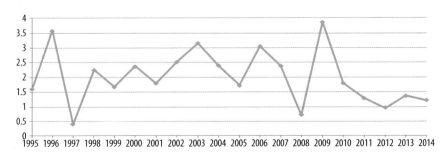

UKBMS population trend

2005-2014
1995-2004

PEACOCK
Aglais io

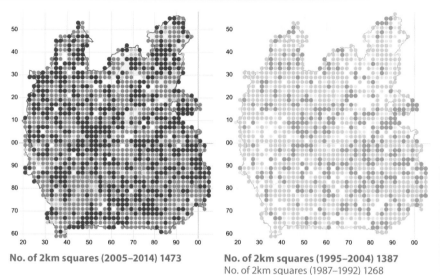

No. of 2km squares (2005–2014) 1473

No. of 2km squares (1995–2004) 1387
No. of 2km squares (1987–1992) 1268

DISTRIBUTION TREND
Increase (6%) ⬆

POPULATION TREND
Minor decrease (2%)

STATUS
National: Low priority
Local: Low priority

HABITAT
Wide-ranging

THREATS
None Known

The striking and ubiquitous Peacock butterfly occurs throughout our three counties, although numbers vary from year to year, with low points in 2011 and in the poor summer of 2012 which is apparent in the population trend (see graph). The slight increase in distribution in the 2005–14 period may be the result of an increase in recording effort rather than a change in distribution.

Peacock larvae.

Their distinctive black spiny larvae can be found in large nettle patches. The parasitoid *Sturmia bella* (see page 37) affects Peacock as well as Small Tortoiseshell larvae. However, *S. bella* is considered not to be the major Peacock parasitoid with an estimate of 15% of larva groups affected, less than the impact of other native parasitoids (Gripenberg 2011).

In our area, Peacock can be found in nearly every month; the first garden record for 2014 was 16th February and the last was 29th November.

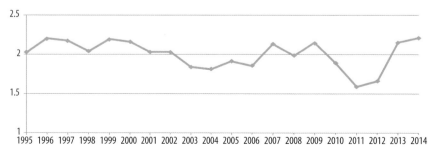

UKBMS population trend

2005-2014
1995-2004

| Jan | Feb | Mar | Apr | May | Jun | Jul | Aug | Sep | Oct | Nov | Dec |

SMALL TORTOISESHELL
Aglais urticae

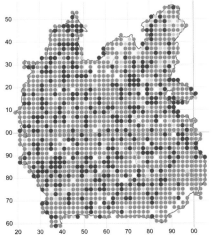

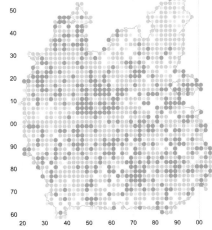

No. of 2km squares (2005–2014) 1487

No. of 2km squares (1995–2004) 1412
No. of 2km squares (1987–1992) 1414

DISTRIBUTION TREND
Increase (5%) ⬆

POPULATION TREND
Decline (8%)

STATUS
National: Low priority
Local: Low priority

HABITAT
Wide-ranging

THREATS
Not fully understood

Small Tortoiseshell is a common garden butterfly, attracted to buddleia. Its population dipped between 2000 and 2012, with a major recovery since 2013 (see graph).

The parasitic fly *Sturmia bella* specialises in attacking nymphalid larvae, and was first recorded in the UK in 1998, just before start of the decline in 2000. It lays microscopic eggs on the surface of nettle leaves and these are ingested by Small Tortoiseshell larvae as they feed. Survival in batches of larvae affected by *S. bella* was between 25% and 48% lower than those without the parasite (Gripenberg 2011). However, our 2005 atlas noted a similar recovery in 1982 from a downturn (before the arrival of *S. bella*), suggesting that fluctuations of this butterfly are complex and not fully understood.

Sturmia bella.

Small Tortoiseshell larvae.

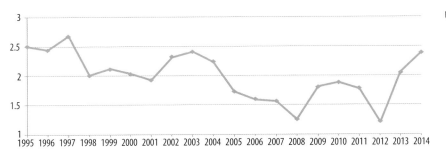

UKBMS population trend

| Jan | Feb | Mar | Apr | May | Jun | Jul | Aug | Sep | Oct | Nov | Dec |

2005-2014
1995-2004

COMMA
Polygonia c-album

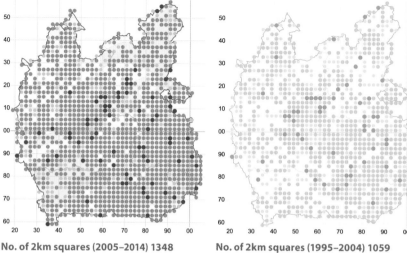

No. of 2km squares (2005–2014) 1348

No. of 2km squares (1995–2004) 1059
No. of 2km squares (1987–1992) 889

DISTRIBUTION TREND
Increase (27%) ⬆

POPULATION TREND
No change

STATUS
National: Low priority
Local: Low priority

HABITAT
Woodland / gardens

THREATS
None known

KEY ACTIONS
None

The Comma has shown an ongoing increase in range over the past three decades with a 19% increase between 1987–1992 and 1995–2004 and a 27% increase between 1995–2004 and 2005–2014. Comparing the 2005–2014 and 1995–2004 distribution maps, there has been an increase in range in the north and west of our three counties and now Comma appears evenly distributed throughout our region.

During the first half of the 19th century, Comma was a common butterfly in Britain, but after a major decline, by 1900 it was restricted to Herefordshire, Worcestershire and Monmouthshire. Numbers have now recovered and Comma can be found in any English county and has spread across much of Wales and far into Scotland. Historically described as using hop as its main foodplant, its increase has been associated with its use of nettle as a much more abundant alternative. Comma is spreading northwards rapidly in Britain; this is thought to be attributable to climate change.

In the UK there are two generations. Eggs laid by Comma butterflies emerging from hibernation early in the year develop quickly and produce a mid-summer generation. This mid-summer form is called *hutchinsoni* which does not hibernate and has lighter underwings than the over-wintering generation. Eggs laid later on in the spring and by the summer generation, produce a late summer brood which will hibernate ready for the following spring.

It is a common garden butterfly, seen in 84% to 94% of gardens in the last ten years, and 20% to 44% of churchyards, in the respective Upper Thames surveys.

Comma, form *hutchinsoni*.

Jan	Feb	Mar	Apr	May	Jun	Jul	Aug	Sep	Oct	Nov	Dec

2005-2014
1995-2004

MARSH FRITILLARY
Euphydryas aurinia

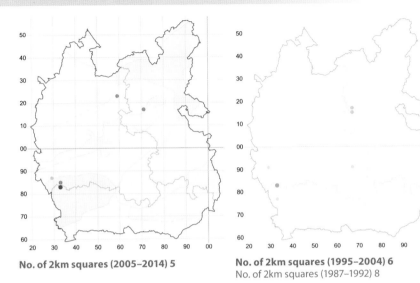

No. of 2km squares (2005–2014) 5

No. of 2km squares (1995–2004) 6
No. of 2km squares (1987–1992) 8

DISTRIBUTION TREND
Decline (17%) ⬇

STATUS
National: High priority
Local: High priority

HABITAT
Calcareous grassland and damp meadows

THREATS
Habitat fragmentation, Loss of foodplant, Overgrazing

KEY ACTIONS
Maintain managed grazing in remaining sites

Marsh Fritillary has been in long-term decline across south-east England, including in our region. In the period 1995–2004, Marsh Fritillary had two known populations, one on a railway cutting near Rushbeds Wood and the other on the Lambourn Downs. Individuals (assumed to be vagrants) were also seen at Swyncombe Down in 1996, at Watts Reserve, south of Lambourn, in 1998 and south of Fernham in 2004.

The population near Rushbeds became extinct after 1996 when the last records were made. In the more recent ten-year period, the population persisted at Seven Barrows. A nest of larvae found at Gavray Drive in Bicester in 2005 led to two adult sightings the next year, but nothing subsequently. This was assumed to be as a result of a release, as were sightings at Westcott.

The remaining population at Seven Barrows has been in decline over the last decade – the site is small and supports only a limited number of suitable individuals of its preferred foodplant (devils-bit scabious). Management of this small site is a challenge. After a period with no grazing, when grasses have become more rank, BBOWT (who manage the site under agreement with the landowner) have been grazing using low numbers of Dexter cattle.

Numbers fluctuate strongly from year to year (as they do elsewhere) through variation in weather, degree of larval parasitism and condition of foodplants. In 2014, only four adult butterflies were seen in our region. We know from elsewhere in Britain that Marsh Fritillary needs access to a much larger landscape of suitable sites than we currently have available in the Lambourn area, to enable it to move between sites that come in and out of suitable condition, to avoid inbreeding and to sustain a viable meta-population. Here, the variations in condition of this site and its isolation may render it unsuitable for the butterfly to persist. The future of the last known population of this beautiful insect in our three counties is at severe risk.

Jan	Feb	Mar	Apr	May	Jun	Jul	Aug	Sep	Oct	Nov	Dec

2005-2014
1995-2004

DUKE OF BURGUNDY
Hamearis lucina

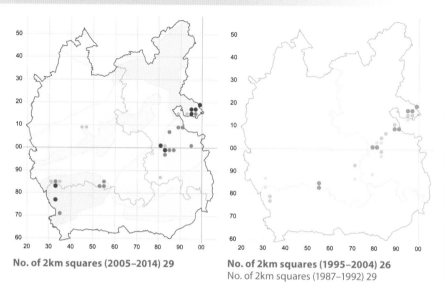

No. of 2km squares (2005–2014) 29

No. of 2km squares (1995–2004) 26
No. of 2km squares (1987–1992) 29

DISTRIBUTION TREND
Increase (12%)

STATUS
National: High priority
Local: High priority

HABITAT
Calcareous grassland with cowslips and ample shelter from scrub; formerly in woodland with primroses

THREATS
Scrub invasion; over-grazing

KEY ACTIONS
Restore suitable grass-scrub mosaic habitats

Duke of Burgundy is one of the Britain's most threatened butterflies, occurring in small populations mainly across southern England. Since 1980, 62% of colonies have gone extinct across Britain, and population abundance measured by transects has declined by 42% since 1976. It is now found on only 120 sites nationally, many of which are vulnerable.

Within our region, the distribution remained apparently steady at between 26 and 29 occupied 2km squares in each survey period between 1987 and 2014. It has declined markedly more recently, with only 20 occupied squares in 2010–14, some of which are singleton records, likely to be vagrants. In central Oxfordshire, two individuals were reported from Wytham Woods in 2005, but none since. We have lost colonies from BBOWT's Dancer's End and Grangelands reserves in Buckinghamshire, and from Aston Upthorpe in Oxfordshire.

In Buckinghamshire, Duke of Burgundy is now limited to a strong colony at Ivinghoe Beacon, a medium-sized colony at Bradenham and a similarly sized colony on a privately owned nature reserve. It is now known at only one site in Oxfordshire (near Berkshire border). Populations survive on three sites on the Lambourn Downs in Berkshire, including one private site specially managed for this butterfly. A successful re-establishment was made at an old site at Bradenham in 2012 and the adult emergence in 2015 was the largest to date. Further introductions may be considered to suitable sites elsewhere.

Conservation work involving scrub clearance continues at remaining sites, including a private site in Buckinghamshire where occasional individuals have been recorded. The long-term future of this, and other private nature reserves, is uncertain due to changes of ownership. In 2014, Butterfly Conservation appointed a 'Duke in the Chilterns' project officer to assist the butterfly's recovery. This recovery requires a network of sites with cowslips (the main larval foodplant), longish grass and scattered scrub.

Jan	Feb	Mar	Apr	May	Jun	Jul	Aug	Sep	Oct	Nov	Dec

2005-2014
1995-2004

SMALL COPPER
Lycaena phlaeas

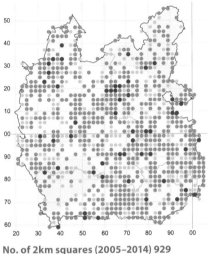

No. of 2km squares (2005–2014) 929

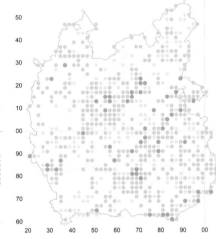

No. of 2km squares (1995–2004) 682
No. of 2km squares (1987–1992) 695

DISTRIBUTION TREND
Increase (36%) ⬆

POPULATION TREND
No change

STATUS
National: Low priority
Local: Low priority

HABITAT
Occurs in a wide variety of habitats. Commonly found on chalk or unimproved grassland, heathland, woodland clearings, waste ground and moorland. Warm, dry conditions are favoured

THREATS
None

Small Copper occurs throughout the Upper Thames region but favours sparsely vegetated habitats such as chalk or unimproved grassland, heathland, woodland clearings, waste ground and moorland. The recorded occupancy of 2km squares increased by 36% between 1995–2004 and 2005–2014, with colonisations occurring throughout the region. There is no clear trend in abundance from monitoring at transect sites and no clear trend in reports from gardens.

A vibrant and distinctive butterfly, it has brilliant copper wings with black spots and borders. It is typically found in small discrete colonies with only a few individuals seen together. Adults can be seen from April to October, with at least two broods per year, and a third usually produced in our region. Numbers reach a maximum in the second brood, with late July and early August the best time to see this species. Eggs are mainly laid on common sorrel or sheep's sorrel and the species survives the winter as a caterpillar.

The conservation priority for Small Copper is to retain areas of rough grassland in warm, sheltered sites. Numbers tend to be high during warm summers although drought conditions can be detrimental as later broods favour small sorrel plants growing in warm spots. Greater frequency of extreme temperatures in some future climate change scenarios may have a detrimental effect on the breeding success of second and third broods of this species.

Jan	Feb	Mar	Apr	May	Jun	Jul	Aug	Sep	Oct	Nov	Dec

2005-2014
1995-2004

BROWN HAIRSTREAK
Thecla betulae

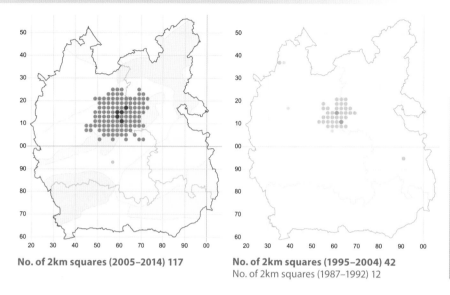

No. of 2km squares (2005–2014) 117

No. of 2km squares (1995–2004) 42
No. of 2km squares (1987–1992) 12

DISTRIBUTION TREND
Major increase (179%) ⬆

STATUS
**National: High priority
Local: High priority**

HABITAT
Scrub/Hedgerow/Woodland edge

THREATS
**Excessive hedgerow cutting;
Deer browsing**

KEY ACTIONS
Sympathetic management of blackthorn hedgerows and field margins

Searching for eggs of Brown Hairstreak in winter has proved to be the best way to monitor this species. If we were reduced to using adult sightings alone to assess the butterfly's fortunes, we would be describing an infrequently seen species, largely restricted to a few well-known sites. Indeed, adults are so infrequently seen that standardised transect monitoring is not suitable for estimating trends in its abundance. However, dedicated searching, within and just beyond the boundaries of its known range, for the small white eggs on blackthorn in winter when it is leafless, has shown a clear expansion. Egg counts in areas that at one time produced no records (despite several years of search effort), show the species appearing and then persisting. Simultaneously, a smaller number of formerly occupied squares have been vacated. Within our region, Brown Hairstreak is found wherever there are suitable corridors of blackthorn, in an area centred on Otmoor, between Oxford, Bicester and Waddesdon near Aylesbury. It even reaches into the centre of Oxford, especially around the old meadows along the Cherwell.

Flying from late July/early August to late September/early October, the Brown Hairstreak is initially very hard to locate while the adults assemble for mating high in sheltered tree-tops. Then, while males remain in the tree canopy, females become more visible as they scatter widely along woodland edges and hedges at lower levels, searching for sheltered blackthorn bushes (and other *Prunus* species) on which to lay their eggs.

Egg-laying females are usually identified quite easily but, within tree-tops and in flight, conclusive identification is much more difficult due to possible confusion with Purple Hairstreak or Speckled Wood in the canopy. Seen against a bright sky these species are difficult to tell apart. In flight, the far commoner Vapourer moth also looks similar. Thus, 'adult' records are ideally supported by photographic evidence.

Eggs are normally laid singly, and less often in small numbers – up to six have been seen together – along young stems and often in the joint between a lateral shoot and the main stem of young growth. Females seem to find very young sucker growth particularly suitable, and eggs are laid to within a few inches of ground level.

The two additional maps here show the contrast between adult sightings and egg sightings, shown at a 1km square resolution – there are nearly four times the number of recorded 1km squares for egg sightings (332) compared to adult sightings (88). We rely heavily on egg sightings, which usefully extend the recording season over 4–5 winter months, to enable us to understand the local distribution.

Jan	Feb	Mar	Apr	May	Jun	Jul	Aug	Sep	Oct	Nov	Dec

2005-2014
1995-2004

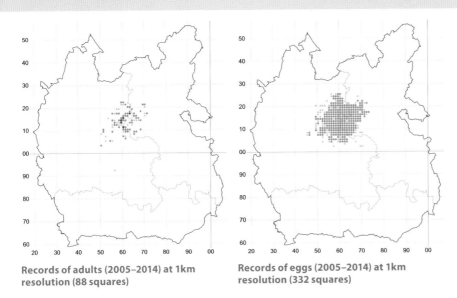

Records of adults (2005–2014) at 1km resolution (88 squares)

Records of eggs (2005–2014) at 1km resolution (332 squares)

Why the population abundance has risen so dramatically (egg numbers by over 1700%) since the 1980s is unclear. Certainly, annual hedge flailing had a hugely detrimental impact and relaxation of this practice has aided recovery. At the same time, the sterling efforts of a determined band of egg-searching volunteers has located colonies in many new 2km squares. This has gone hand in hand with successful encouragement to land managers to cease annual trimming of all their blackthorn and to allow some young suckers to grow into field margins.

Searching for eggs of Brown Hairstreak (Otmoor 2013).

Brown Hairstreak egg.

PURPLE HAIRSTREAK
Favonius quercus

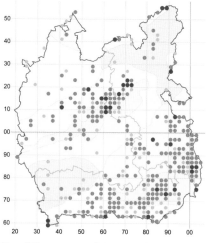
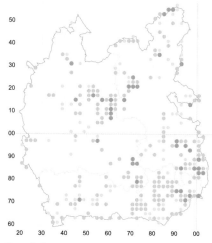

DISTRIBUTION TREND
Increase (14%) ⬆

POPULATION TREND
No change

STATUS
**National: Low priority
Local: Low priority**

HABITAT
Woodland, Scrub/Hedgerow

THREATS
**Habitat fragmentation,
Excessive hedgerow cutting**

KEY ACTIONS
**Better recording to assess its
true status**

No. of 2km squares (2005–2014) 352

No. of 2km squares (1995–2004) 309
No. of 2km squares (1987–1992) 226

Almost the entire life of Purple Hairstreak is spent high in oak trees. Almost any sizeable oak, even solitary trees, can hold Purple Hairstreak, although trees that have been isolated for a long time may be less likely to retain populations. This behaviour makes this species hard to spot and is likely to result in it being under-recorded. It often needs lengthy observation of the tops of oak and ash trees through binoculars to determine its presence (it breeds in oaks but frequently takes aphid honeydew from ash trees).

Variation in skills between recorders at spotting this elusive butterfly, along with its unsuitability for transect recording makes interpretation of trends in this species uncertain. Despite a 14% increase in the number of 2km squares where it was recorded over the last ten years, this increase has not been steady. Although abundant until 2011, the period 2010–14 shows a fall in reports (to just 221 2km squares).

The main flight period of this species appears to have advanced by about a week between the two recording periods, probably due to climate warming along with earlier bud burst.

The Purple Hairstreak is far more likely to be recorded by surveyors actively searching for it. We believe that the species quite possibly exists in every 2km square where large oaks grow. There is a risk if larger oaks are removed, without being replaced, of isolating the remaining populations to distances that are beyond their powers of dispersal.

Targeted surveys of 'blank' 2km squares, beginning with areas that border known colonies should be conducted to see if the species is losing ground within the Upper Thames region, perhaps supplemented with systematic egg-hunts in winter. Where possible, oaks should be planted, to fill gaps between existing trees with colonies.

Purple Hairstreak egg laid on an oak bud.

2005-2014
1995-2004

GREEN HAIRSTREAK
Callophrys rubi

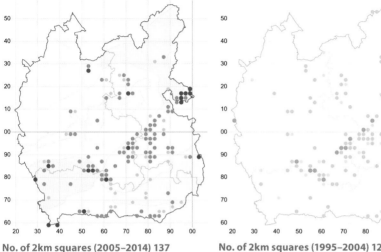

No. of 2km squares (2005–2014) 137

No. of 2km squares (1995–2004) 126
No. of 2km squares (1987–1992) 78

DISTRIBUTION TREND
Increase (9%) ⬆

POPULATION TREND
Decline (6%)

STATUS
National: Medium priority
Local: Low priority

HABITAT
Scrubby grassland; woodland
rides/ clearings; heathland;
railway cuttings; old quarries

THREATS
Scrub invasion; overgrazing;
overshading in woods

KEY ACTIONS
Maintain suitable grass-
scrub mosaic habitats

Green Hairstreak is widespread but local, both nationally and in our region, occurring in small colonies in suitable habitat throughout the three counties. However, it is easily overlooked because it is well camouflaged when sitting with wings closed (which they invariably are) among foliage. The Chilterns and the Berkshire Downs contain many local strongholds for the butterfly, where semi-natural grassland is interspersed with medium-sized bushes. The number of occupied squares and the general distribution are similar in the two ten-year periods. The number of occupied squares recorded in the last two five-year periods is also almost constant at around 100. Transect data show that the population trend of Green Hairstreak is variable but with a slight decline of 6% since 1995.

The persistence and wide distribution of Green Hairstreak may in part be due to its broad use of larval foodplants, including rockrose, bird's-foot-trefoil, dyer's greenweed, gorse and broom, allowing it to switch foodplant if necessary and colonise dissimilar nearby habitats. Scrub and bushes are essential both for shelter, and to give the males high vantage points to defend their territories and seek females.

It is the UK's only truly green-coloured butterfly. Although the iridescent green underside of the wings is distinctive when perching, in flight the dull brown of the upperside is more apparent, and it can be confused with other species. The white 'hairstreak' on the underside is highly variable; in 2011, two of our members (Chris and Pat Dennis) had the distinction of discovering a new aberration, named after them ab. *Dennisorum* (Campbell, 2011).

Green Hairstreak shares habitat and flight season with Grizzled and Dingy Skippers, and the three species can often be found together – a triple treat early in the butterfly year. Although the distribution seems to be reasonably stable, care must be taken to ensure that its present sites become neither too overgrown, nor overgrazed.

Green Hairstreak *ab. Dennisorum.*

| Jan | Feb | Mar | Apr | May | Jun | Jul | Aug | Sep | Oct | Nov | Dec |

2005-2014
1995-2004

WHITE-LETTER HAIRSTREAK
Satyrium w-album

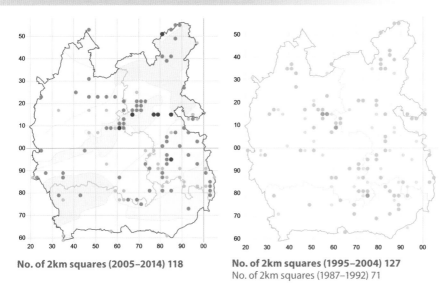

No. of 2km squares (2005–2014) 118

No. of 2km squares (1995–2004) 127
No. of 2km squares (1987–1992) 71

DISTRIBUTION TREND
Decline (7%)

STATUS
National: High priority
Local: Medium priority

HABITAT
Scrub/hedgerow, woodland

THREATS
Dutch Elm Disease, excessive hedgerow cutting

KEY ACTIONS
Maintain remaining elms, consider planting of resistant elms

White-letter Hairstreak seems to have become a much more elusive species in our area in recent years. Populations crashed in the late 1970s when elm trees (the sole foodplant) were devastated by Dutch Elm Disease. After a worrying period in the 1980s there was a resurgence in the 1990s, and signs that lost ground was being re-colonised (on sucker re-growth). This is reflected in the number of recorded squares in 1995–2004, but the small drop in 2005–14 hides a paucity of records in the last five years (with only 56 squares) masked by better years in 2006 and 2010. Currently, the species is faring badly and in our region most reports in the last three years were of single butterflies. These were mainly in the east with a continual retraction from the south west over the last 15 years. There were several sites in our area where you could be fairly confident of finding White-letter Hairstreak, often nectaring on thistles or brambles. It is now difficult, in most parts of our area, to recommend where to go locally to see this butterfly.

White-letter Hairstreaks spend most of their lives around the tops of trees and with a flight period of about a month, it is almost certainly under-recorded and not suited to detection through transect monitoring. Data for our region are insufficient to make any reliable estimate of population sizes or longer term trends.

Records show that the flight period (shown below) appears to be about two weeks earlier in 2005–14 than it as in 1995–2004, potentially a response to climate warming.

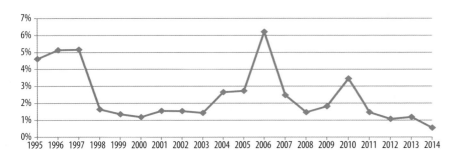

Occupancy – % recorded squares with White-letter Hairstreak

2005-2014
1995-2004

Dutch Elm Disease (DED) is a fungal disease, transmitted by elm bark beetles, which carry the fungal spores (Gibbs 1994). The beetles only lay under mature bark. This allows elms to grow for about 15 years before the bark is thick enough for the beetles to bore in, leaving spores that infect, and subsequently kill, the tree. This may explain the cyclic nature of White-letter Hairstreak abundance since 1980. DED often spreads along a line of elms in a hedgerow (which may all be parts of the same plant, extending by putting up new suckers). Planting disease-resistant elm species (as has been done at Holtspur Bottom reserve) may provide a more stable food supply in the medium term, but as females prefer to lay their eggs on large trees (see photo), new plantings will be slow to show benefits.

Both known and potential sites need to be monitored both for the butterfly and for the continued presence of suitable elm trees. Spring surveys for larvae may be more productive than summer searches for adults, in determining range and frequency. Currently, the species is present in such low numbers that it is hard to detect; sightings from most sites are not repeated in subsequent years. A ten-year survey report may be painting an unrealistically rosy picture. A national project has been operating for some years, run by Liz Goodyear and Andrew Middleton from Herts and Middlesex branch (see http://www.hertsmiddx-butterflies.org.uk/w-album/index.php) to better understand the distribution and dynamics of this species, and they have provided valuable assistance in site surveys for this species in our region.

White-letter Hairstreak laying eggs.

Egg of White-letter Hairstreak on elm twig.

BLACK HAIRSTREAK
Satyrium pruni

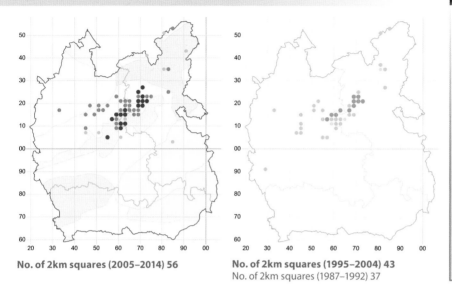

No. of 2km squares (2005–2014) 56

No. of 2km squares (1995–2004) 43
No. of 2km squares (1987–1992) 37

DISTRIBUTION TREND
Increase (30%) ⬆

STATUS
National: Medium priority
Local: High priority

HABITAT
**Woodland, scrub/hedgerow/
woodland edge**

THREATS
**Too frequent hedge flailing
and habitat fragmentation**

KEY ACTIONS
**Continue efforts to detect
and then maintain all
colonies**

Although the larval foodplant, blackthorn, of Black Hairstreak is common in southern England, the range of this butterfly in the UK is highly localised to the narrow clay belt between Oxford and Peterborough. Currently there are 76 occupied sites in Oxfordshire and Buckinghamshire, but none in Berkshire. These two counties hold about half of the known national populations of Black Hairstreak, so we have a special responsibility in this area to conserve our populations.

Regular searches for this species reveal large annual fluctuations in numbers detected. On average, records kept by our species champion indicate that about three adults are typically detected for each hour spent searching known locations, although numbers detected in the poor summer of 2012 were markedly lower. Increased effort to locate this species has produced a better knowledge of its ability to exist at low population densities in hedgerows that had previously been deemed to have insufficient cover of older blackthorn to maintain Black Hairstreak populations. The increase in the number of 2km squares with records and the number of known colonies may therefore partly reflect increased recorder effort rather than increased butterfly numbers. Further, current sampling methods such as transect walks are considered unsuitable to reliably assess change in population size for this species.

Searches for the grey-coloured eggs of Black Hairstreak are far less successful than searches for the bright white eggs of Brown Hairstreak, and the few sightings of Black Hairstreak eggs have mainly occurred during egg searches for the latter. In areas where the two species are known to overlap, fewer than one Black Hairstreak egg is typically seen for every hundred Brown Hairstreak eggs seen. The additional maps here, both shown at 1km resolution, contrast sightings of Black Hairstreak eggs (nine squares in 2005–14) with adult sightings (54 squares in 2005–14). It is possible, with searching, to find pupae – they develop usually on the upper side of a leaf and resemble bird droppings (see photo). The combination of a short flight season and the challenges of finding immature stages make this a difficult species to detect and more difficult to establish trends over short time periods. We therefore rely more heavily on longer-term data sets to understand changes in its distribution and abundance.

A period of relatively high abundance in the mid-1980s led to an extension of range in west Oxfordshire, but numbers subsequently fell around the millennium with an associated retraction in range. Similarly, there has

Jan	Feb	Mar	Apr	May	Jun	Jul	Aug	Sep	Oct	Nov	Dec

2005-2014
1995-2004

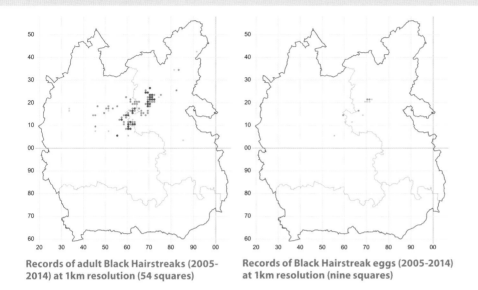

Records of adult Black Hairstreaks (2005-2014) at 1km resolution (54 squares)

Records of Black Hairstreak eggs (2005-2014) at 1km resolution (nine squares)

been dynamic colonisation and extinction of sites in Buckinghamshire during the last 20 years. Encouragingly, the species has been detected at several nature reserves in north Buckinghamshire where appropriate habitat management should ensure their survival. More broadly within the region, concerted efforts to preserve thick hedges containing older blackthorn continue across the butterfly's range. An additional priority is to establish a more robust approach to assess the population status of this species in the Upper Thames region.

Black Hairstreak egg.

Black Hairstreak pupa.

SMALL BLUE
Cupido minimus

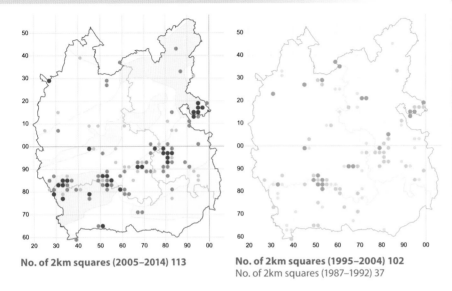

No. of 2km squares (2005–2014) 113

No. of 2km squares (1995–2004) 102
No. of 2km squares (1987–1992) 37

DISTRIBUTION TREND
Increase (11%) ⬆

STATUS
National: Medium priority
Local: Medium priority

HABITAT
Calcareous grasslands

THREATS
Habitat fragmentation &
Scrub invasion

KEY ACTIONS
Habitat maintenance /
creation

The Small Blue distribution appears stable within our area, with similar numbers of occupied 2km squares in the survey periods. However a more detailed analysis of the 2005–2014 recording period shows significant variation in the reported 2km squares from year to year, so under-reporting of this small butterfly is likely.

In the three counties, Small Blue mainly occurs on the Chilterns and Downs; there are a few records from the mid-vale ridge and the Cotswolds. In good years, Small Blues can occur in high numbers. We know of counts of over 100 from Swyncombe Down, Pitstone, East Hagbourne and Bradenham. When conditions are right and their foodplant (kidney vetch) is available, new colonies can establish, as at our Holtspur reserve, with eight sightings in 2013 and 24 in 2014. Small Blue appears sedentary, typically forming small colonies of fewer than 30 individuals. Mark-recapture studies show that adults rarely move more than 40 metres, but a few travel over one kilometre (Bourn 2000).

The best habitats for this species are dry sheltered grasslands with kidney vetch present and a mosaic of short and tall vegetation including light scrub. Small Blue depends on continued presence of kidney vetch. This plant, an early colonist of disturbed soils, struggles to compete with grasses and scrub, and fares best in areas of short vegetation. Only periodic ground disturbance (or very poor soils) will allow it to persist. The adult butterflies roost on stems of the longer grasses in sheltered areas with higher vegetation, emphasising the importance of a varied habitat structure to this species. Small Blues depend on the plants to be in flower when they lay eggs, which are usually laid singly. One good site in 2007 had so few plants in flower, when the adults emerged, that multiple eggs (over 20) were laid on each flower (see photo).

Multiple Small Blue eggs on a kidney vetch flower head.

Jan	Feb	Mar	Apr	May	Jun	Jul	Aug	Sep	Oct	Nov	Dec

2005-2014
1995-2004

HOLLY BLUE
Celastrina argiolus

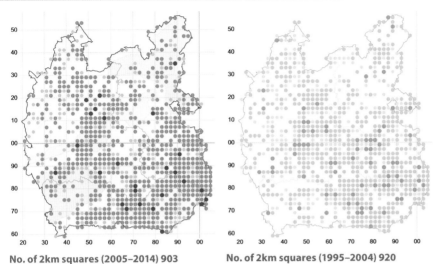

No. of 2km squares (2005–2014) 903

No. of 2km squares (1995–2004) 920
No. of 2km squares (1987–1992) 1130

DISTRIBUTION TREND
Minor decline (2%) ⬇

POPULATION TREND
Decline (6%)

STATUS
National: Low priority
Local: Low priority

HABITAT
Widespread: possibly more common in gardens

THREATS
None

KEY ACTIONS
Maintain flowering female holly trees and mature flowering ivy in gardens, churchyards, parkland

This attractive little butterfly is widespread across our region, and is a regular visitor to gardens, churchyards, hedgerows and parkland. In both ten-year periods it was more prevalent in the south-eastern half of our region, perhaps reflecting the pattern of urbanisation. It flies in early spring, with mated females searching for holly trees on which to lay their eggs. The larvae eat developing flowers and berries of these and various other flowering shrubs, possibly making gardens more attractive to this butterfly than the wider countryside. Second-brood butterflies appear in late summer, when the females seek ivy for egg-laying.

Holly Blue abundance is affected by a tiny host-specific parasitic wasp that lays eggs singly in young larvae (Revels 1994), with a wasp emerging from up to 90% of pupae. This reduces Holly Blue abundance, which in turn reduces wasp numbers, subsequently allowing butterfly numbers to increase again. Numbers of Holly Blues fluctuate with peaks and troughs in a cycle typically lasting three to six years, as shown by our garden and churchyard surveys and transect abundance. The cycle was strong until about 1999, when the depth of the troughs decreased for unknown reasons, but recent data suggests that the trough may be deepening again.

Assuming that numbers recover again as the cycle progresses, this colourful butterfly is likely to remain widespread and a frequent garden visitor.

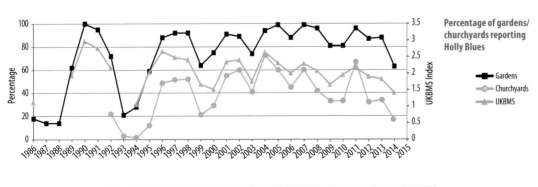

Percentage of gardens/ churchyards reporting Holly Blues

— Gardens
○ Churchyards
▲ UKBMS

2005-2014
1995-2004

SILVER-STUDDED BLUE
Plebejus argus

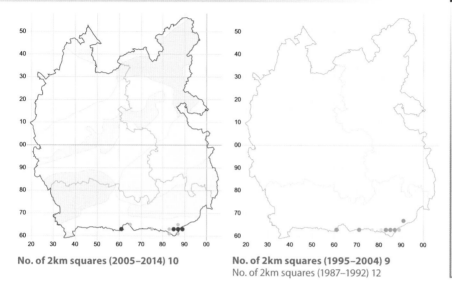

No. of 2km squares (2005–2014) 10

No. of 2km squares (1995–2004) 9
No. of 2km squares (1987–1992) 12

DISTRIBUTION TREND
Increase (11%) ⬆

STATUS
National: High priority
Local: High priority

HABITAT
Heathland on the southern Berkshire border

THREATS
Lack of suitable management to produce a succession of pioneer heathland

KEY ACTIONS
Introduce rotational heather management

This delightful little butterfly, a "flagship" species of lowland heaths, is confined to small remnants of heathland in Berkshire. Our sites form part of a larger population whose stronghold is the larger heathlands of north-east Hampshire and north-west Surrey.

Since 1800 we have lost nearly 85% of lowland heath in the UK. This combined with lack of suitable management on what remains and the loss of chalk downland colonies has reduced the butterfly's range by over 90% nationally. We believe that our Berkshire population has suffered a similar decline.

Many of the smaller colonies in the Greenham area, at Decoy Heath, Padworth Common, Wokefield Common, Wellington College and Kings Ride have been lost, leaving only colonies at Wildmoor, Broadmoor Bottom and Wishmoor Bottom. For a number of years this species appeared to be lost from Wildmoor but then reappeared. We suspect that it was overlooked during this period rather than being absent. Whilst the data show an increase in number of 2km squares since 1995–2004, the most recent five-year period shows a greater than 50% drop to only four squares.

In the UK, only the Large Blue butterfly has a stronger association with ants. The precise choice of egg-laying site, the protection of caterpillars, pupae and adults (during emergence) are all governed by the presence of black ants (*Lasius niger* and *L. alienus*). Thus conservation management of this species is as much about the ants' requirements as it is about the butterfly's needs.

The overall loss of our heathlands seems to have been halted but the rather uniform management of the remainder does not suit this butterfly. We need to work with land managers to introduce rotational management both where it persists and on adjoining areas, to encourage a mosaic of vegetation heights, including the young pioneer heathland that this sedentary butterfly requires.

Jan	Feb	Mar	Apr	May	Jun	Jul	Aug	Sep	Oct	Nov	Dec

2005-2014
1995-2004

BROWN ARGUS
Aricia agestis

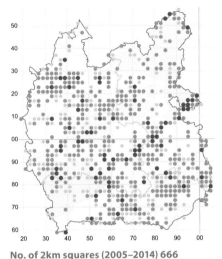

No. of 2km squares (2005–2014) 666

No. of 2km squares (1995–2004) 378
No. of 2km squares (1987–1992) 163

DISTRIBUTION TREND
Major increase (76%)

POPULATION TREND
Minor increase (1%)

STATUS
National: Low priority
Regional: Low priority

HABITAT
Calcareous grassland, open dry grassland

THREATS
Habitat loss and fragmentation

KEY ACTIONS
Good grassland management

Formerly, the Brown Argus was mostly confined in our region to the chalk grassland of the Downs and Chilterns, where its preferred foodplant, common rock-rose, occurs. More recently, with improving climatic conditions for this species, it has been found to breed 'off the chalk', using foodplants of the *Geranium* and *Erodium* genera (for example crane's-bill and stork's-bill species), reflecting a wider national pattern.

This trend can be detected in the distribution maps. In the earlier ten-year period it was largely confined to calcareous grassland areas including the Downs and Chilterns, with a more widespread distribution in the recent ten-year period. As a result, the number of 2km squares in which Brown Argus has been recorded has increased by 76% between the two periods. However, there are indications that, in years with less favourable weather, its distribution retreats to the core calcareous habitats where common rock-rose occurs. Garden survey data and transect monitoring shows large variation in the annual reports, we assume as a result of periodic retreat to its core habitat.

Male and female Brown Argus butterflies resemble female Common Blues, which usually have little or no blue on their wings. Thus identifying this butterfly is more challenging than for 'Blues' with bright blue males and it may be under-recorded as a result. Even though the distribution of Brown Argus may be increasing, we need to maintain habitat quality, otherwise population sizes on existing sites may be reduced.

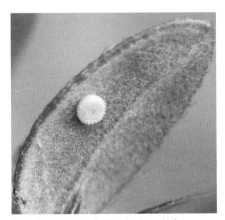

Brown Argus egg on underside of rock-rose leaf.

Jan	Feb	Mar	Apr	May	Jun	Jul	Aug	Sep	Oct	Nov	Dec

2005-2014
1995-2004

COMMON BLUE
Polyommatus icarus

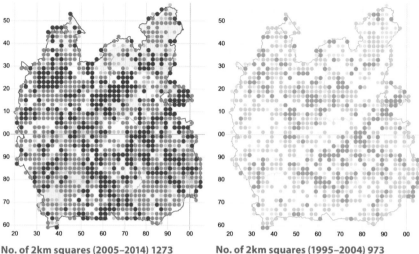

No. of 2km squares (2005–2014) 1273

No. of 2km squares (1995–2004) 973
No. of 2km squares (1987–1992) 893

DISTRIBUTION TREND
Increase (31%) ⬆

POPULATION TREND
No significant change

STATUS
National: Low priority
Local: Low priority

HABITAT
Calcareous grassland,
pasture/meadow, ruderal/
setaside

THREATS
Overgrazing, undergrazing,
scrub invasion

KEY ACTIONS
Maintain herb-rich
grassland

Common Blue is the most widespread blue butterfly in the British Isles, as it is reasonably mobile and readily exploits opportunities to establish new colonies. These qualities are probably linked with the ability of its foodplants (primarily bird's-foot-trefoil and black medick) to thrive on recently disturbed soils and in managed grasslands.

All three local recording periods have confirmed Common Blue's presence as a widespread butterfly throughout the three counties. Some years with poor weather (e.g. 2012) yield fewer records but the same is true of other years for no such obvious reason. Whilst these year-to-year variations are puzzling, it is encouraging that data from transects show no long term weakening in numbers.

Common Blue is a less frequent garden visitor than Holly Blue, but was still reported from between 30% and 73% of gardens in UTB surveys over 2005–2014. The flight period for both broods appears to start a few days earlier on average in 2005-14 than it did in 1995–2004.

The butterfly needs larval foodplants in a warm short turf, with taller grasses for roosting. It is therefore commonest in areas of scrub-free grassland of mixed sward height where its foodplants thrive. Such habitat is often transitory but a resilient Common Blue colony will often persist in reduced numbers in non-ideal conditions.

Consequently, the future of Common Blue in our three counties seems secure. However, there are threats, including an increase in vegetation growth (linked to higher soil fertility from atmospheric pollution) leading to cooler positions for foodplants within the turf, and an increasing tendency to tidy the countryside. Removal of tall vegetation suitable for roosting may lead to loss of ideal habitat. If lengthy adverse weather conditions were to coincide with one of the unexplained periodic dips in numbers, this butterfly's position as one of our most widespread species may be weakened.

Jan	Feb	Mar	Apr	May	Jun	Jul	Aug	Sep	Oct	Nov	Dec

2005-2014
1995-2004

ADONIS BLUE
Polyommatus bellargus

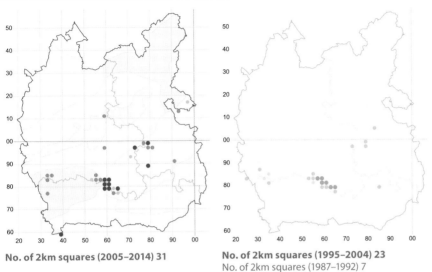

No. of 2km squares (2005–2014) 31

No. of 2km squares (1995–2004) 23
No. of 2km squares (1987–1992) 7

DISTRIBUTION TREND
Increase (35%) ⬆

STATUS
National: Medium priority
Regional: High priority

HABITAT
Calcareous grassland

THREATS
Reduction in grazing, overgrazing, scrub invasion, habitat fragmentation

KEY ACTIONS
Maintain managed grazing in short turf with horseshoe vetch

The number of sites with records of Adonis Blue is higher after 2000 than before, although some of the recently gained ground has been lost in the last four years. Even so, it is now known from more locations than at the time of our first atlas for the Upper Thames region and with some previously temporary sites being more regularly occupied. It remains local in our area.

Most of the new colonies for this species are in the Chilterns and on the Wiltshire/Berkshire border. Their appearance (some distance from established sites) suggests either early pioneers in a range expansion or clandestine releases. Since colonising these outlying sites, small populations have generally been maintained.

The two core sites for Adonis Blue in our region are adjacent to the Goring Gap. Stragglers from these colonies are recorded in adjacent squares in most years and may ultimately result in sustained populations.

Adonis Blue egg on horseshoe vetch leaf.

Changes, both climatic and in site management, may create the warmer conditions the larvae require. Further south in England such changes have benefited populations of Adonis Blue but sufficient warmth is unreliable this far north and tends only to be found on nature reserves with south-facing slopes and which are specifically managed to provide warm microclimatic conditions. So, while a gradual expansion in range is possible, there is also a threat of local extinctions due to a lack of suitable site management, a run of cool weather or by the isolation of sites. Should some sites suffer a major population crash, the distance to neighbouring colonies may, in many cases, be too far to allow re-colonisation. Consequently, a priority for this species is to work with land managers to promote appropriate management of sites, both to promote persistence of colonies as well as increasing the area of intervening land in suitable condition to provide 'stepping stones' between sites.

| Jan | Feb | Mar | Apr | May | Jun | Jul | Aug | Sep | Oct | Nov | Dec |

2005-2014
1995-2004

CHALKHILL BLUE
Polyommatus coridon

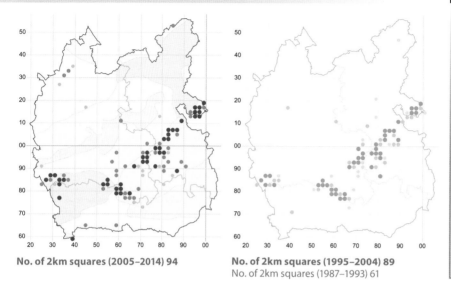

No. of 2km squares (2005–2014) 94

No. of 2km squares (1995–2004) 89
No. of 2km squares (1987–1993) 61

DISTRIBUTION TREND
Increase (6%) ⬆

STATUS
National: Low priority
Local: Medium priority

HABITAT
Calcareous grassland

THREATS
Scrub invasion, Habitat fragmentation, Overgrazing

KEY ACTIONS
Maintain managed grazing

The local range of Chalkhill Blue has remained relatively stable between 1995 and 2014, with some expansion into new areas within the existing range after conservation management has made sites more suitable. The core breeding sites known during the earlier atlas period 1995–1999 are still present. In our three counties, the population breeds almost exclusively on chalk grassland under some form of conservation management, and in particular, along the scarp slopes of the Chilterns and some grazed areas of the Downs. However, Chalkhill Blue colonies on sites with a northerly aspect have experienced gradually falling numbers, while similar habitats with southerly aspects have rising numbers. This suggests that the condition of the larval foodplant, horseshoe vetch, during the early instars is crucial. The growth of taller grass and scrub is more likely on cooler, damp north facing slopes. This shades (and further cools) the foodplant, and is believed to be detrimental.

A proportion of adults (usually males) wander, sometimes many kilometres, from their breeding colonies. This can give the impression of small, temporary colonies. Continued monitoring is essential to confirm establishment, such as has been demonstrated near the BBOWT Dancers End reserve (BBOWT) and at the Butterfly Conservation Holtspur Bottom reserve. At College Lake (BBOWT), Horseshoe Vetch was planted in 1998 and although breeding was evident in 2000 there has been no further evidence of breeding despite continued monitoring.

Several consecutive poor summers could reduce the number of colonies and the more isolated sites would be unlikely to be re-colonised until overall numbers recover. Making marginal north-facing sites more suitable, along with improving the condition of south facing slopes, where sites are generally more favourable for this species, is key to the species persistence and spread. Butterfly Conservation engages with local land managers to ensure that the butterfly's needs remain in focus.

Jan	Feb	Mar	Apr	May	Jun	Jul	Aug	Sep	Oct	Nov	Dec

2005-2014
1995-2004

EXTINCT AND IRREGULAR MIGRANT SPECIES

Extinctions

Since the first account of the butterflies within our region we have lost several species. In "The State of Butterflies in Berkshire, Buckinghamshire and Oxfordshire" (2005) we had already acknowledged the loss of both Small Pearl-bordered Fritillary (last seen in 1990) and Pearl-bordered Fritillary (last seen in 1995) and we may have to acknowledge in due course the loss of Wall as a breeding species too.

Between 2010 and 2014, records of Wall have suggested vagrant butterflies and not breeding colonies.

Rare Migrant Species

Migrant species are very varied in their pattern of occurrence, dependent on breeding success outside UK and large-scale weather patterns. For some species, this is complicated by the inappropriate but increased availability of captive-bred non-native butterflies for release at social gatherings. Some species seen during this atlas period could not naturally migrate to the UK and can fairly certainly be described as appearing with some form of human assistance. Sometimes we know about their origins, as when a member (Martin Kennard) found a caterpillar of a South African Orange-banded Protea (*Capys alphaeus*) in a bouquet of imported flowers bought in Oxfordshire, which duly hatched into an adult.

There are 'butterfly houses' at some tourist attraction sites, such as Blenheim Palace. These invariably contain exotic tropical species, because they are both showier and easier to breed continuously than British species. Occasionally a few individuals may escape and they have been seen within a short distance from the hot-house, although we are not aware of any escapees taking up permanent residence in our colder climate.

Orange-banded Protea.

Far trickier are the reports of species that don't normally migrate to our region but conceivably could. Continental swallowtails are rare visitors to the UK and sometimes take up temporary residence near the south coast. This species bred in a Buckinghamshire garden in 2014 with at least three adults resulting but we strongly suspect that the parent female had been released. About the same time that these offspring were seen, a Swallowtail of unknown origin appeared in an Oxfordshire garden.

There is a similar difficulty with Camberwell Beauty. Normally, this species is extremely scarce even along the east coast (where it is most frequent) but occasional irruptions, when large numbers enter the country, can result in it become widespread. During such an event in 2006 it appeared in each of our three counties. It was seen again in 2014 (solely Oxfordshire) but not during any major movement from Europe.

Sadly, it seems that this species is destined to remain an occasional visitor as it (like the Peacock) lays its eggs after hibernating through the winter and the Camberwell Beauty seems unable to overwinter successfully in the UK.

Camberwell Beauty.

DATA AND DATA ANALYSIS

We have provided two main analyses of the data collected for this atlas – distribution trends (analysed from general site/species records) and population trends, analysed principally from transect data (UKBMS including the WCBS).

The table shows the number of 2km squares visited in each period, the percentage of visited squares in which each species has been recorded (occupancy) and the change in occupancy in the two main atlas periods, 1995–2014 and 2005–2014. We also show the occupancy (Occ) in the four consecutive five-year periods between 1995 and 2014.

	2005–2014		1995–2004			1995–99	2000–04	2005–09	2010–14	UKBMS
Squares visited:	1557		1559			1519	1347	1551	1554	Trend
Species:	Squares	Occ	Squares	Occ	Change	Occ	Occ	Occ	Occ	1995–2014
Dingy Skipper	144	9.2%	116	7.4%	24%	5.9%	5.9%	6.5%	7.4%	-0.2%
Grizzled Skipper	115	7.4%	125	8.0%	-8%	6.5%	5.9%	5.5%	6.0%	-1.5%
Essex Skipper	706	45%	871	56%	-19%	46%	28%	26%	33%	-14% ***
Small Skipper	1114	72%	1178	76%	-5%	64%	45%	50%	58%	-15% ***
Silver-spotted Skipper	22	1.4%	22	1.4%	0%	0.9%	1.3%	1.4%	0.8%	
Large Skipper	1093	70%	1038	67%	5%	54%	44%	46%	59%	-2.5% *
Wood White	18	1.2%	32	2.1%	-44%	1.8%	1.1%	0.8%	0.8%	
Orange-tip	1301	84%	1253	80%	4%	68%	52%	63%	69%	-0.1%
Large White	1537	99%	1452	93%	6%	83%	68%	94%	87%	2.0%
Small White	1535	99%	1456	93%	6%	83%	72%	91%	93%	-2.1%
Green-veined White	1505	97%	1453	93%	4%	84%	68%	87%	87%	-0.5%
Clouded Yellow	296	19%	328	21%	-10%	12%	16%	9%	14%	
Brimstone	1350	87%	1217	78%	11%	65%	57%	64%	77%	-0.5%
Wall	22	1.4%	114	7.3%	-81%	6.3%	2.6%	0.8%	0.6%	
Speckled Wood	1436	92%	1335	86%	8%	74%	66%	82%	75%	1.0%
Small Heath	430	28%	475	30%	-9%	27%	15%	19%	20%	1.1%
Ringlet	1363	88%	1235	79%	11%	64%	56%	66%	76%	1.9% *
Meadow Brown	1526	98%	1508	97%	1%	89%	75%	88%	92%	-0.1%
Gatekeeper	1478	95%	1464	94%	1%	84%	66%	79%	86%	-3.2% **
Marbled White	1020	66%	864	55%	18%	46%	39%	43%	53%	-1.8%
Grayling	25	1.6%	25	1.6%	0%	1.4%	1.1%	1.4%	1.2%	
Pearl-bordered Fritillary	0	0.0%	1	0.1%	-100%	0.1%	0.0%	0.0%	0.0%	
Silver-washed Fritillary	373	24%	68	4.4%	449%	3.2%	2.4%	11.4%	21.0%	47% *
Dark Green Fritillary	126	8.1%	103	6.6%	22%	6.0%	3.2%	4.3%	6.8%	-10% **
White Admiral	194	12%	143	9.2%	36%	7.2%	5.4%	7.7%	8.9%	-3.5%
Purple Emperor	150	10%	45	2.9%	234%	2.0%	1.9%	4.5%	8.1%	
Red Admiral	1324	85%	1185	76%	12%	65%	51%	62%	73%	-2.5%
Painted Lady	1204	77%	836	54%	44%	40%	38%	71%	31%	-7.3%
Peacock	1473	95%	1387	89%	6%	79%	60%	76%	87%	-2.4%
Small Tortoiseshell	1487	96%	1412	91%	5%	82%	65%	69%	89%	-8.3% *
Comma	1348	87%	1059	68%	27%	54%	49%	67%	73%	-0.1%
Marsh Fritillary	5	0.3%	6	0.4%	-17%	0.3%	0.1%	0.3%	0.1%	
Duke of Burgundy	29	1.9%	26	1.7%	12%	1.6%	1.0%	1.3%	1.3%	
Small Copper	929	60%	682	44%	36%	34%	29%	39%	46%	-0.3%
Brown Hairstreak	117	7.5%	42	2.7%	179%	0.7%	3.0%	5.5%	7.3%	
Purple Hairstreak	352	23%	309	20%	14%	14%	11%	15%	14%	-0.3%
Green Hairstreak	137	8.8%	126	8.1%	9%	6.6%	5.8%	6.3%	6.7%	-5.7% *
White-letter Hairstreak	118	7.6%	127	8.1%	-7%	6.8%	3.3%	5.4%	3.6%	
Black Hairstreak	56	3.6%	43	2.8%	30%	1.8%	2.2%	3.1%	2.5%	
Small Blue	113	7.3%	102	6.5%	11%	4.9%	4.5%	4.8%	4.7%	
Holly Blue	903	58%	920	59%	-2%	48%	41%	41%	44%	-5.7%
Silver-studded Blue	10	0.6%	9	0.6%	11%	0.6%	0.3%	0.6%	0.3%	
Brown Argus	666	43%	378	24%	76%	18%	16%	25%	32%	1.2%
Common Blue	1273	82%	973	62%	31%	50%	45%	56%	68%	-0.6%
Adonis Blue	31	2.0%	23	1.5%	35%	1.1%	1.2%	1.6%	0.9%	
Chalkhill Blue	94	6.0%	89	5.7%	6%	4.6%	4.6%	4.5%	4.6%	

Distribution of species

The following two graphs show the ten most widespread species in our area and the ten most localised species, respectively, based on occupancy (percentages of visited squares in which each species was recorded), derived from the 2005–2014 records.

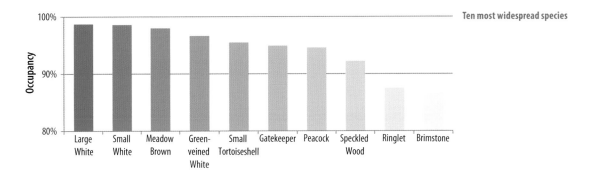

The most widespread species are, not surprisingly, those that have relatively easily met needs in commonly available habitat patches throughout our area (and across most of the country). They are frequently recorded in gardens.

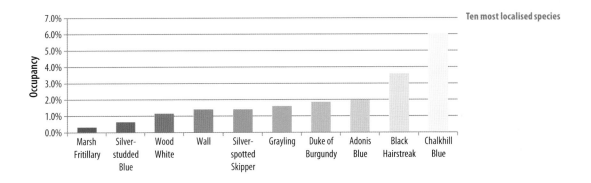

Our most localised species are habitat specialists for which only a limited number of sites in our area provide their particular requirements. We should be particularly concerned about those at the lower end of this graph – these are species occupying only a handful of sites, at significant risk and on the brink of extinction in our area. We work to ensure that the relevant landowners of such sites are made aware of these high priority species and that appropriate management is strongly recommended. The other species also face threats and need our care and management to ensure that they do not slip into the higher risk zone.

A summary of the changes in range (occurrence), shown in the graph below, shows that a majority of species have increased in occurrence over the last decade, with eleven species showing net losses in range.

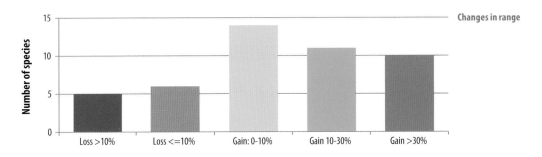

The graphs below show the top five winners and losers, in terms of distribution change (changes in occurrence).

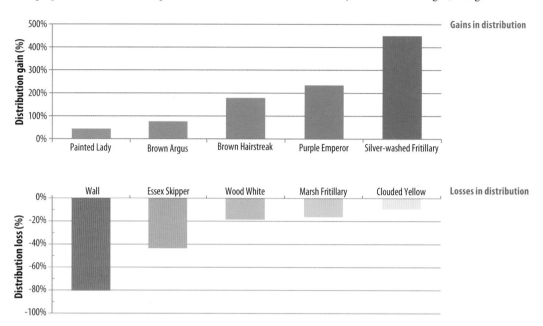

Changes in abundance

We also show, at the right of the table on page 58, the changes in abundance (population trend) derived from the UKBMS transect monitoring data, for the 20-year period 1995–2014. The asterisks show statistical significance (* $p<0.05$, ** $p<0.01$, *** $p<0.001$). Note that we have population data for only 30 out of the 46 species recorded, and only some are statistically significant.

Transect counts provide an annual estimate of the abundance of a butterfly species at each monitored site, using a standardised sampling method (see www.ukbms.org). Each site index provides a relative measure of the actual population size, sampling a proportion of the number of butterflies actually present. Site indices are combined to derive collated indices for our area using a statistical model to estimate population trends over time. These show, in effect, how the average population density of each species has changed year by year on monitored sites.

If butterflies breed more successfully on monitored sites, there is an increase in the numbers recorded (and the corresponding index) and the population trend (or abundance) increases. If breeding success is reduced, the index and the abundance trend decrease.

The graph below shows that, in contrast to the distribution trend, more species have decreased in abundance than have increased between the two ten-year survey periods. Only six species show an increase in abundance, whereas 24 have a negative trend.

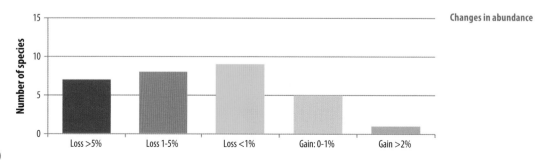

The graphs below show the top five winners and losers, in terms of population trend.

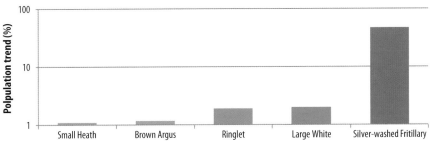

Population trend positive

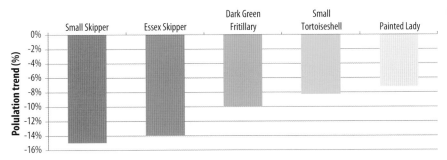

Population trend negative

Our conclusions in the species accounts relate to whether each species is expanding or contracting in range (or remaining stable); and whether it is increasing, decreasing or stable in abundance on monitored sites. In interpreting these, we need to be aware of the limitations of recording methods and that some apparent changes may not be statistically significant.

In many cases, changes appear to be correlated – increases in abundance sometimes occur alongside increases in range (e.g. Silver-washed Fritillary), or vice versa (e.g. Essex Skipper). We do not have a population trend for Wood White, but non-transect records indicate diminishing numbers. However, there are species that are increasing in range, but decreasing in abundance (e.g. Dark Green Fritillary, White Admiral and Green Hairstreak), although there are none showing a significant increase in population with a reduction in distribution. Many different factors, ranging from internal biology to external environment, affect butterfly ranges and populations; in some cases, factors driving an increase in range may be opposed by factors reducing populations on individual sites.

We should be concerned about conservation of all the most localised species (see page 59), and we should be most concerned for those species that are also showing the largest reductions in range and/or negative population trend – Marsh Fritillary, Wood White and Wall.

The resulting combination of factors affecting each species is unique to that species and interpretation of observed changes is therefore a challenge. Nevertheless there are strong indications of factors that broadly affect a number of species in similar ways, such as: range expansions consistent with impacts of climate change; and population decreases attributable to loss of traditional woodland, grassland or heathland management.

Marsh Fritillary.

Wood White.

Wall.

CLIMATE CHANGE

Changes in flight periods and climate change

There has been much discussion in publications by Butterfly Conservation and others about impacts of climate change on butterflies. There are several examples of species moving further north in Britain that are attributed to the effects of climate warming enabling breeding at progressively higher latitudes (see for example: Asher *et al.* 2000; Fox *et al.* 2011; and Fox *et al.* 2015). Many species appear to be responding in this way, where they have the means to colonise new areas of suitable habitat within flying range. Shifts in range visible at a national scale are less apparent at a local scale, although shifts in flight period are visible locally.

Clouded Yellow has overwintered along the most sheltered sections of England's south coast in recent years with milder winters. Red Admiral is now overwintering and seems able to survive most winters across large areas of England and probably along south facing coasts in Wales and Scotland too. These are perhaps other manifestations of climate warming.

For each species in this atlas, a bar graph shows the flight period in 1995–2004 and 2005–2014. Although about half the species show little difference between the flight periods, about half show a flight period starting earlier in the year, and in some cases also continuing later in the year in the more recent period. Amongst those showing greater flight period differences are Grizzled Skipper, Wood White, Orange-tip, White-letter Hairstreak and the example below, Silver-washed Fritillary, which shows both an earlier start to the flight period and a longer period, extending to later dates.

Flight periods for Silver-washed Fritillary.

Amongst the factors affecting flight periods, climate warming is amongst the more compelling. For species whose development is at least partly governed by temperature, and using their flight periods in countries with warmer climates as a guide, we would expect higher average temperatures to bring emergence dates forward, and for the flight period to last for longer.

There are species, such as Gatekeeper (see below), for which there is no evident change in the start of the flight period, although there may be a small extension to the period. It is possible that the development of such species is governed more by a factor such as day length, in which case we would not expect to see much influence of climate warming.

Flight periods for Gatekeeper.

How will future climate change affect butterflies?

Many factors may affect butterflies and climate change is only one. Habitat loss has undoubtedly been a major factor driving butterfly species decline to date. In future, climate change will become increasingly important. Most climate change experts expect that average global temperatures will continue to rise for decades to come. Measures to reduce greenhouse gas emissions will take a long time to be delivered and for their impact to become effective. Experts also consider that climate change will not just increase average temperatures, but will also result in greater extremes of weather, and more frequent storms.

Although increasing temperatures may appear to offer advantages to butterflies, greater turbulence in our weather will put additional pressure on species at a time when many other factors are posing threats. We will need to remain vigilant in future years and continue to monitor our butterflies to ensure that our conservation strategies remain as effective as possible.

BUTTERFLY HABITATS

Saving butterflies means conserving suitable habitats

Butterflies are an enigmatic mix of fragility and resilience. We appreciate their fragility as they fly about in the sun and yet heavy rain, and even frost, may have little ill effect. As soon as it dries and warms up, they fly around again.

However, whilst these are obvious features of their adult lives, they are perhaps less crucial than several factors affecting the earlier life stages. Generally speaking these stages have limited mobility and so must begin life in the right place. Unable to make their own body heat, or to travel far to find the essential warmth, moisture and nutrients that they need, eggs, caterpillars and pupae will only thrive if they find themselves in a position that provides them with a suitable combination of all three. Unless a caterpillar hatches in precisely the right habitat (a place that protects and nourishes it as it completes its life cycle) it will not survive.

For many of our commonest species, the 'right habitat' (one which provides essential resources) is now a man-made environment. For example, man-made grassland is common in the Upper Thames Branch area, because it suits us and our livestock to maintain large areas of grassland. Consequently, we see more members of the 'Brown' family of grass-feeding butterflies, than most others. However, the corollary is that these butterflies suffer when artificially created and maintained grasslands are removed as a result of intention or neglect.

Meadow Brown is numerous and widespread as its caterpillars are adapted to feed on a variety of commonly available grass species. Where grasses grow in soil that is sun-warmed but not parched, the caterpillars thrive. In slightly warmer positions, they can grow fast enough to fly as adults in June and in slightly cooler positions they develop more slowly and can emerge to fly as late as September.

Other species have adapted to habitats that are less frequently found and, consequently, they are scarcer. Even though the caterpillars of Silver-spotted Skipper also feed on grasses, it is scarce in our area. This is because it can only eat one species of grass (sheep's fescue), and only develops where the local microclimate keeps it very much warmer than ambient temperature. At temperatures that suit Meadow Brown, Silver Spotted Skipper would be too cold to develop. Temperatures that suit a flourishing Silver-spotted Skipper caterpillar may not suit a Meadow Brown caterpillar. Even though both species can feed on grasses, they need to find it in different microclimates.

Comparing these butterfly species illustrates that the presence of a food plant is not enough. That plant must be growing in precisely the right habitat too. A challenge for conservationists is how to provide for a multitude of species when each needs unique conditions. The solution may lie in an approach described below.

Comma caterpillar.

Ringlet– one of the brown species which has perhaps benefitted from widespread grassland.

The answer, in so far as there is one, is to look at the underlying geography of our region and work with it. Some parts of the UTB area will never be able to support certain butterfly species because the soil is too acid or too alkali to allow the growth of the necessary foodplants in the right condition. In other places, the ground slopes steeply towards or away from the sun, which plays a large part (but not the only part) in determining the temperatures these slopes will experience, particularly in spring. Large areas have a dominant vegetation type with associated turf heights and degrees of shade because of factors such as drainage, soil nutrient levels, or type of grazing livestock and it is far more sensible to work with the resources that are present. Thus, efforts to conserve the Silver Studded Blue will be centred on the gravel-based soils south of Reading as this is primarily a butterfly of heathland habitats in UK.

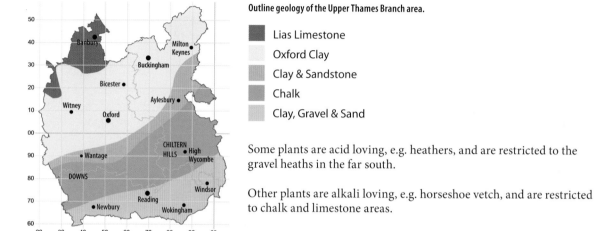

Outline geology of the Upper Thames Branch area.

- Lias Limestone
- Oxford Clay
- Clay & Sandstone
- Chalk
- Clay, Gravel & Sand

Some plants are acid loving, e.g. heathers, and are restricted to the gravel heaths in the far south.

Other plants are alkali loving, e.g. horseshoe vetch, and are restricted to chalk and limestone areas.

In the past, nature reserves were often described as "islands of biodiversity", isolated in a sea of hostile landscape – a situation now more technically referred to as habitat fragmentation. Individual nature reserves may go in and out of suitable condition over a long period of time, and local extinctions of particular species can occur when conditions have become unsuitable for a few seasons. The recognition that larger areas of habitat, or a network of suitable sites in close proximity, are a vital component of a strategy for conserving a wide variety of plant and animal species led to the promotion of the concept of landscape-scale conservation, being strongly advocated by Butterfly Conservation (Ellis *et al.* 2012) and other conservation organisations. This approach is based on identifying key habitat features in our landscapes and promoting ways to link suitable sites with other similar habitat patches by appropriate management of the land between them. These linkages in our landscapes make it possible for species to migrate through the landscape and enable the population of previously unoccupied habitat patches. Individual sites that become unsuitable temporarily and lose key species can be replenished naturally when they return to favourable condition from near-neighbouring habitat patches holding these species. Landscape-scale conservation therefore improves species' resilience.

The way in which habitats are linked with the underlying geology is recognised by Natural England in a similar approach to conservation through Natural Character Areas (NCAs) – see page 7 for details.

So, while conservation organisations still work to maintain quality habitat within existing sites with interesting biodiversity, they also try to influence management of the land bordering those sites, especially where separate sites with high diversity of particularly threatened key species can be more closely connected.

The constant work to maintain good quality habitats

Maintaining habitat for butterflies means ensuring that the required foodplants are available in large quantities in zones with appropriate temperatures and humidities.

Removing grass after mowing improves floral diversity.

In grassland this means grazing (or mowing and raking) to regulate grass length and scrub density. A mix of light scrub and areas with grass of varied turf height provides refuge areas against wind chill for eggs, caterpillars, pupae and roosting adults.

The right timing of grazing and mowing is part science and part experience. Each year, the growing season will be different and the prescription to produce the healthiest habitat will vary. It is generally true that aiming to produce a variety of turf heights and densities across the site will best cater for vagaries in the weather and the responses of the plants.

Similarly, woodlands need intervention to maintain the best habitat for butterflies. Unmanaged rides will slowly develop longer grass and more aggressive weeds before turning to scrub. Even if these deleterious impacts are prevented, the continual growth of trees on the south side of any ride will gradually increase the shade and reduce the temperature at ground level.

Woodland: after thinning, to allow light to penetrate and warm the ground flora.

Although the need to check the negative impacts posed by over-shading are required less frequently than in grassland (with its faster growth rate), there is a real benefit from clearing small portions of the tree growth within woodland each year on a rotational basis. This way there is always a variety in the temperatures, humidity and plants growing most strongly in the wood. A few species (e.g. Purple Emperor) require large trees, so decisions on which trees are removed to allow light and warmth to the ground should be considered carefully.

Commercial forestry dictates that many woods are managed irregularly by machines. Large areas may be unmanaged for a number of years but then large contiguous areas are felled. This can create – but often also removes – resources that butterflies rely upon. As in farmed environments, where the retention of grassy margins around fields provide habitats around crops, woodlands are more often managed with conservation areas between commercially worked timber and these can act as refuges and connections between purposefully maintained wildlife habitats.

Hedgerows have always been valued for their wildlife but the most recent studies of the Hairstreak species has shown that they utilise hedgerows to a far greater extent than was imagined. A gradual reduction in the flailing of hedges has permitted them to grow taller and thicker, concurrent with a rise in the number of hedgerows

Intensive agriculture.

identified as holding populations of Black and Brown Hairstreak; two of Britain's rarest butterfly species with nationally important populations in our region.

Sadly, most of the agricultural land stretching from around Reading towards Newbury, and between Oxford, Aylesbury and Milton Keynes, is intensively farmed and generally inhospitable to butterflies due to a much reduced range of suitable habitats.

Our work with nature reserves

Holtspur Bottom

Evidence of the success of targeted conservation effort comes from our own reserve at Holtspur Bottom just outside Beaconsfield. Here, arable reversion has successfully created habitat for short turf, downland butterflies. Small Blue and Chalkhill Blue butterflies have moved in and established colonies, as shown by the transect counts for these species in recent years.

Transect counts	2009	2010	2011	2012	2013	2014	2015
Small Blue	2	0	0	0	2	18	15
Chalkhill Blue	0	0	0*	8	12	7	37

*Chalkhill Blue first appeared in 2011 but in numbers so low that the transect failed to detect them. Similarly, Small Blue was present on site between 2009–2013 but in small numbers.

The numbers of the pre-existing Dingy Skipper and Brown Argus have also increased in number. Essex Skipper, Green Hairstreak, Purple Hairstreak and Small Copper are regularly seen as are many commoner species and migrants such as the Clouded Yellow in years when it comes to the UK in good numbers.

The rare Striped Lychnis moth continues to breed on the reserve and measures are in place to increase the area of the habitat that this species requires. A scheme began in 2014 to distribute the seeds of its Dark Mullein foodplant to residents in the area around Holtspur Bottom and more widely within the moth's range. Over 500 seedlings were planted on the reserve and we are hoping the population of the moth (which is surveyed by counting its larvae and has returned figures of approximately 30–40 larvae for the last three years) will rise as a result of the extra foodplants available.

Striped Lychnis moth larva.

Surveying the yellow heads of dark mullein flowers for Striped Lychnis larvae, at Holtspur Bottom.

The uninspiring field at Holtspur Bottom in 2008.

Changes at the reserve are not limited to the increasing number of key butterflies but also (and presumably because of) changes in the flora. Volunteers have changed monotonous fields into floristically diverse meadows. The reserve now serves to demonstrate techniques of arable reversion and meadow management to others.

In the photograph above, the grassland on the opposite hillside (Holtspur Bank reserve) with its variety of colours, shows how varied that is in contrast to the Holtspur Bottom field, as it was in 2008. Compare this with the flower-rich appearance of the same field (from a slightly different vantage point) in 2010.

Holtspur Bottom in June 2010.

All the changes at Holtspur have been achieved with the sustained efforts of about 40 volunteers over many years. Their efforts have paid a handsome reward. Information about the reserve, its plants and animals, can be found at http://holtspurbottom.info/index.html.

Aston Upthorpe Downs

We continue to work to maintain habitat by selective scrub clearance at Aston Upthorpe Downs in south Oxfordshire, another downland habitat reserve. This site comprises interlinked valleys in the chalk downland, with a mix of open grassland, partial woodland and scrub cover.

This is a former site of the Duke of Burgundy which seemed to disappear around 2006 although occasional sightings have been reported more recently. Silver-spotted Skipper used to occur in one of the valleys, Juniper Valley, but has disappeared possibly as a result of sheep grazing at the wrong time over 2–3 flight seasons and has not been recorded there since 2009.

Juniper Valley.

Several habitat specialists continue to thrive there, including Dingy and Grizzled Skipper and Chalkhill Blue. We also receive less regular reports of Dark Green Fritillary and Small Blue. Green Hairstreak does well in these valleys, particularly where there is some larger scrub adjacent to open areas of grassland. We are grateful to the landowner, Mr Anthony Allen, for providing access and for his assistance and cooperation with our conservation work on this site.

There is little doubt that some high quality chalk grassland habitat would now have disappeared under developing scrub if our branch had not been managing the important slopes there.

Work party at Aston Upthorpe.

Site work on Duke of Burgundy

One of the most threatened UTB species, the Duke of Burgundy, has been successfully returned to a former site in the Chilterns by one of our members (Ched George) working together with the National Trust. It is now breeding there again.

In 2014, UTB funded a 'Duke in the Chilterns' Project Officer to assist in recovering this species from the brink. A measure of the branch's determination to secure our rarest species was illustrated when more people volunteered to help with habitat creation work for this species than was deemed safe for the site where we hoped to get them working!

Duke of Burgundy.

Good news

Despite the continuing threat to butterflies from further development and the associated loss of semi-natural habitats in the south east of England, there are further signs that conservation efforts are starting to produce results. Better knowledge about the requirements of key species and improved expertise in delivering the habitat management to meet those needs, has stabilised or improved the number of colonies of about half of our habitat specialists. This is largely attributed to improved management of existing habitat and partly through a combination of creation of new habitats and climate change.

Gains in occupancy of 1km squares by *habitat specialists* (1995–2004 to 2005–2014)

Silver-washed Fritillary +507%

Brown Hairstreak +248%

Purple Emperor +206%

Black Hairstreak +43%

Dingy Skipper +29%

Adonis Blue +29%

Dark Green Fritillary +18%

Chalkhill Blue +15%

Small Blue +14%

Increasing evidence of the importance of a free flow of butterflies between areas of habitat strongly supports the movement towards landscape-scale conservation. This is encouraging as butterflies live in dynamic ecosystems, where no habitat is permanently suitable. Fortunately, research shows that sub-optimal (so-called 'marginal') habitat can act as a stepping stone between 'ideal' habitats, assisting dispersal to higher quality habitat provided these habitats are relatively close together.

There are several examples of land being reverted to a more diverse state around the region. One is at Greenham Common where initially The Greenham Common Trust worked to restore heathland habitat and now the Berkshire, Buckinghamshire and Oxfordshire Wildlife Trust (BBOWT) has taken over the management (in 2014), with a grant of £10,000 towards their Linking the Landscape Project. This aims to safeguard wildlife habitats by linking them more closely together; in this case, with the adjacent Bowdown Woods, Crookham Common, and Thatcham Reedbeds. Previously, there was a danger that each separate site tried to host several habitat types, and that some were perhaps too small to be truly effective. A larger acreage allows management to concentrate on those parts of all the formerly smaller sites which are the most likely to support high quality examples of particular habitat types.

M40 Compensation area (2007).

Locally, we enjoy good relations with key wildlife and related organisations, working jointly on a number of projects and having an influence well beyond our size through the impact of our detailed reports, advice and expertise. Many bodies consult us where planned development may have a detrimental impact on biodiversity.

Even the creation of new roads and improved rail links offers opportunities for butterfly conservation. The building of the M40 led to the creation of a 'Compensation Area' to the east of Bernwood Forest adjacent to the motorway. Here a former arable field was taken out of food production and was developed to become the densest colony of Black Hairstreak butterflies in the country. The planned re-opening of the Oxford to Bletchley rail line is also taking butterfly populations into account, with various measures employed to mitigate potential damage and enhance existing populations by creating new habitat.

Impacts of development

However, this evidence of a new realisation of the need to consider wildlife more thoughtfully during development doesn't mean that we can be complacent about the threats to butterflies. Pressure from the government to see massive numbers of new houses (and all the associated roads, schools, and the other infrastructure associated with housing) means that many areas of remaining undeveloped land are under consideration for some type of development. Though few schemes will destroy key habitats, the ever greater urban sprawl could prevent attempts to link our high quality sites by creating suitable habitat between them, further increasing the isolation of each key site from others and consequently the risk of extinction site by site (as the separating distances are too great to allow natural re-colonisation).

House building.

In 2014, the government announced a £1 billion programme to help unlock 200,000 new homes by funding the required supporting infrastructure. Within our Upper Thames area there are already plans for massive house building programmes. The gov.uk website shows that Buckinghamshire and north Oxfordshire have the highest levels of new house completion in the UK and that the rate of increase in the number of houses is among the country's fastest in north Buckinghamshire and north Oxfordshire. These new houses will include some large developments near Bicester (5,500 homes), around Witney (1,500 homes) and Upper Heyford (1000 homes) in Oxfordshire; near Wokingham, Berkshire (2,000 homes); and Aylesbury, Buckinghamshire (2,450 homes). Planned new house building over the next five years totals about 16,000 in Berkshire, 15,000 in Buckinghamshire, and 35,000 in Oxfordshire.

Whilst there are signs that developers understand that people don't want to live in large areas of concrete, divorced from nature, and are coming forward with more sustainable schemes (such as at the RSPB-guided Kingsbrook development near Aylesbury), there are real worries about continuing large scale developments. The biggest concern is that politicians fail to grasp the importance of landscape scale conservation and fall back on 'traditional' planning approaches. In 2015, as part of their election materials, the Conservatives, Liberals and UKIP all stated that they would prioritise development on brownfield sites. Even the Greens say that they wish to *'minimise encroachment on to undeveloped greenfield sites, wherever possible by reusing previously developed sites that have fallen into disuse'*. So, with grants to developers who use brownfield sites, these are prime targets for building.

Unfortunately for wildlife and biodiversity, many brownfield sites in the UTB area are species-rich, and often sit in the landscape between other areas rich in conservation value, making them ideal for connecting important sites in these landscapes. As an example, the old Pitstone quarries in Buckinghamshire are still home to Biodiversity Action Plan high- and medium-priority butterfly and moth species, despite the building of over 400 homes and 14 light industrial units on the part of the quarry nearest the village centre. Unfortunately, the plan is to extend the building over the majority of the remains of the undeveloped quarry, reducing the value of the site for wildlife.

The records of our members allow us to continue to argue from real evidence on the value of land, no matter how it is popularly conceived and for changes in practices to the advantage of biodiversity.

The undeveloped part of Pitstone quarry.
The yellow flowers are largely kidney vetch and this site and surrounding parts of the old quarries support the largest Small Blue colony in our area.

Overall, it is possible to see that recognition of the damage done to our countryside (and butterfly populations) may have created a climate where political and conservation-based movements are beginning to achieve real improvements in biodiversity. Provided that organisations such as Butterfly Conservation continue to collect data and present it to influential bodies, and to demonstrate how species can be conserved in practice, there is genuine reason to be optimistic that butterflies will continue to delight us in the future.

Recommended Sites in the UTB area are shown below with key species found at each. All sites are open to the public, are free to enter and have car parking.

Berkshire

Greenham Common (SU 500645) – Greenham Common Trust, managed by BBOWT. Heathland with Dingy and Grizzled Skipper; Small Blue and Grayling.

Lardon Chase & Lough Down (SU 589811) – National Trust reserve. Downland with Dingy and Grizzled Skipper; Adonis, Chalkhill and Small Blue; and Small Heath.

Wildmoor Heath (SU 848628) – BBOWT reserve. Woodland and heathland with Grayling and Silver-studded Blue.

Buckinghamshire

Bernwood Forest and Meadows (SP 611117) – Forestry Commission and BBOWT. Mixed Woodland with Black, Brown and Purple Hairstreak; Purple Emperor, Silver-washed Fritillary and White Admiral.

Ivinghoe Beacon (SP 961163) – National Trust reserve. Downland with Dark Green Fritillary, Dingy and Grizzled Skipper; Duke of Burgundy, Chalkhill and Small Blue; Green Hairstreak and Small Heath.

Holtspur Bottom (SU 9189106) – Butterfly Conservation reserve (note: limited parking available) – see www.holtspurbottom.info for more information. Restored downland with Dingy Skipper, Green Hairstreak, Small and Chalkhill Blue; and Small Heath.

Oxfordshire

Aston Rowant (north) SU 732966 and (south) SU 727958 – National Nature Reserve. Downland with Adonis and Chalkhill Blue; Dingy, Grizzled and Silver-spotted Skipper; Dark Green Fritillary, Green Hairstreak and Small Heath.

Otmoor (SP 570126) – RSPB reserve. Wet grassland with extensive hedges, with Black, Brown, Purple and White-letter Hairstreak; and Silver-washed Fritillary.

Warburg (SU 721879) – BBOWT reserve. Woodland and grassland with Grizzled Skipper, Green and Purple Hairstreak; Purple Emperor, Silver-washed Fritillary and White Admiral.

Local Organisations and links

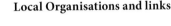

Butterfly Conservation – Upper Thames Branch
www.upperthames-butterflies.org.uk
Twitter: www.twitter.com/UpperThamesBC
Facebook: www.facebook.com/Butterflies.Berkshire.Buckinghamshire.Oxfordshire
Moths recording and discussion forum: www.upperthamesmoths.blogspot.co.uk/
Holtspur Bottom reserve: www.holtspurbottom.info/

BBOWT (the local Wildlife Trust)
The Lodge, Armstrong Road, Littlemore, Oxford, OX4 4XT
Tel: 01865 775476
www.bbowt.org.uk

The Chiltern Society
White Hill Centre, White Hill, Chesham, Bucks, HP5 1AG
Tel: 01494 771250
www.chilternsociety.org.uk

Buckinghamshire and Milton Keynes Environmental Records Centre (BMERC)
www.bucksmkerc.org.uk

Thames Valley Environmental Records Centre (TVERC)
www.tverc.org

National Organisations and links

Butterfly Conservation:
Manor Yard, East Lulworth, Wareham, Dorset, BH20 5QP
Tel: 0870 7744309
www.butterfly-conservation.org

UK Butterfly Monitoring Scheme: www.ukbms.org

UK Butterflies: www.ukbutterflies.co.uk

iRecord Butterflies app: www.brc.ac.uk/article/irecord-butterflies-mobile-app

Biological Records Centre: www.brc.ac.uk

National Biodiversity Network: www.nbn.org.uk

REFERENCES – FURTHER READING

Adey, J.P. and Wilson, S.F. (2010). *The impact of the M40 motorway on populations of Chalkhill Blue Lysandra coridon, and Silver-spotted Skipper Hesperia comma at Aston Rowant National Nature Reserve.* Br. J. Ent. Nat. Hist. 23, 7–19.

Agassiz, D., Beavan, S.D. and Heckford, R.J. (2013). *A checklist of the Lepidoptera of the British Isles. Royal Entomological Society,* St Albans.

Asher, J. (1994). *The Butterflies of Berkshire, Buckinghamshire and Oxfordshire.* Pisces Publications, Newbury.

Asher, J., Warren, M., Fox, R., Harding, P., Jeffcoate, G. and Jeffcoate, S. (2001). *The Millennium Atlas of Butterflies of Britain and Ireland,* Oxford University Press, Oxford.

Asher, J., Bowles, N., Redhead, D. and Wilkins, M. (2005). *The State of Butterflies in Berkshire, Buckinghamshire and Oxfordshire,* Pisces Publications, Newbury.

Bourn, N.A.D. and Warren, M.S. (2000). *Species Action Plan: Small Blue Cupido minimus,* Butterfly Conservation, Wareham, Dorset.

Campbell, W. (2011). *Callophrys rubi (L.) ab. dennisorum Campbell ab. nov. (Lep.: Lycaenidae) Green Hairstreak: A new aberration discovered in Buckinghamshire.* The Entomologist's Record and Journal of Variation, 123, 239–240.

Davies, Z.G., Wilson, R.J., Coles, S. and Thomas, C.D. (2006). *Changing habitat associations of a thermally constrained species, the silver-spotted skipper butterfly, in response to climate warming.* Journal of Animal Ecology 75, 247–256.

Ellis, S., Bourn, N.A.D. and Bulman, C.R. (2012). *Landscape-scale conservation for butterflies and moths: lessons from the UK Butterfly Conservation,* Wareham, Dorset.

Fox, R., Asher, J., Brereton T., Roy, D., Warren, M. (2006). *The State of Butterflies in Britain and Ireland.* Pisces Publications, Newbury.

Fox, R., Brereton, T.M., Asher J., Botham, M.S., Middlebrook, I., Roy, D.B. and Warren, M.S. (2011). *The State of the UK's Butterflies 2011,* Butterfly Conservation and the Centre for Ecology & Hydrology, Wareham, Dorset.

Fox, R., Brereton, T.M., Asher, J., August, T.A., Botham, M.S., Bourn, N.A.D., Cruickshanks, K.L., Bulman, C.R., Ellis, S., Harrower, C.A., Middlebrook, I., Noble, D.G., Powney, G.D., Randle, Z., Warren, M.S. and Roy, D.B. (2015). *The State of the UK's Butterflies 2015,* Butterfly Conservation and the Centre for Ecology & Hydrology, Wareham, Dorset.

Gibbs, J., Brasier, C. and Webber, J. (1994). *Dutch Elm Disease in Britain,* Forestry Commission Research Information Note No.152 Forestry Commission, Edinburgh.

Gripenberg, S., Hamer, N., Brereton, T., Roy, D.B. and Lewis, O.T. (2011). *A novel parasitoid and a declining butterfly: cause or coincidence (Abstract only),* Ecological Entomology (2011), 36, 271–281 – Wiley Online Library.

Joy, J., Williams, M. and Jeffcoate, S. (2010). *Conservation of the Wood White Butterfly (Leptidea sinapis),* Butterfly Conservation Report S10–16, Wareham, Dorset.

Klop, E. *et al.* (2015). *Impact of nitrogen deposition on larval habitats: the case of the Wall Brown butterfly Lasiommata megera,* Journal of Insect Conservation, 19, 393–402.

Lawson, C.R. and Bennie, J.J. *et al.* (2013). *The status and conservation of the silver-spotted skipper Hesperia comma in South-East England 2000–2009.* University of Exeter, Exeter, UK.

Natural England (2014). National Character Areas; see: www.gov.uk/government/publications/national-character-area-profiles-data-for-local-decision-making

Palmer, G. *et al.* (2015). *Individualistic sensitivities and exposure to climate change explain variation in species' distribution and abundance changes,* Science Advances, 1, e1400220.

Pollard, E. (1981). *Population studies of woodland butterflies,* NERC Open Research Library, Centre for Ecology & Hydrology, Wareham, Dorset.

Revels, R. (1994). *The rise and fall of the Holly Blue butterfly.* British Wildlife, 5, 236–9.

Stefanescu, C. *et al.* (2013). *Multi-generational long-distance migration of insects: studying the painted lady butterfly in the Western Palaearctic,* Ecography, 36, 474–486.

Steel, C. and Steel, D. (1985). *Butterflies of Berkshire, Buckinghamshire and Oxfordshire,* Pisces Publications, Oxford.

Van Dyck, H. *et al.* (2015). *The lost generation hypothesis: could climate change drive ectotherms into a developmental trap?* Oikos, 124, 54–61.

NAMES OF RECORDERS

The authors gratefully acknowledge the following people who have contributed records during the recent recording period (2005–2014), which have been used in this atlas:

Peter Abbott, John Acton, Andrew Adams, Mary Adams, Peter Adams, Sally Adams, Shirley Adams, Tracy Adams, Victoria Adams-Stockwin, William Addington, Ken Agutter, Elizabeth Akers, Willem Akkerhuys, Zahra Akkerhuys, Martin Albertini, Elizabeth Alcock, Michael Alcock, Giles Alder, Liz Aldersley, Jeff Alderson, Tara Alderson, Jean Alexander, Sue Alexander, Valerie Alexander, Gemma Alford, Andrew Allan, Carys Allan, Catherine Allan, Alexandria Allen, Arthur Allen, Chris Allen, Daniella Allen, Des Allen, Grace Allen, Janice Allen, Jill Allen, June Allen, Justine Allen, Natalie Allen, Roy Allen, Trevor Allen, Simon Allison, Roy Alliss, Diana Allport, Adrian Allsop, Sally Allsop, Chris Allsopp, Joan Allum, Ian Alston, John Amatt, David Ambrose, Christine Ames, Jean Amor, Ken Amor, Bob Anderson, Kate Anderson, Les Anderson, Daniel Andrew, Richard Andrew, Hayley Andrews, John Andrews, Kathryn Andrews, Dot Angel, Clare Annal, Janet Anstis, Jane Applegarth, Maggie Appleyard, Louise Archer, Nick Archer, Alexander Argent, Christopher Argent, Sallie-Anne Arlington, Abby Armitage, Helen Armstrong, Roger Armsworth, Mary Arnold, Stephen Arnold, Tilly Arnold, Jon Arntzen, Kathryn Ash, Steve Ash, Kate Ashbrook, Lucy Ashby, Ruth Ashcroft, David Asher, Denise Asher, Jim Asher, Nick Asher, John Ashford, John Ashton, Janet Ashwell, Andrew Ashworth, Natasha Askew, R Asprey, Carolyn Aston, Charlotte Aston, Laura Athawes, Val Atkins, Liz Atkinson, Will Atkinson, Rosemary Atmore, Gary Attwood, Hilary Audus, Tom August, Craig Austin, Karen Avery, Alice Ayers, Jo Ayers, Ella Azzopardi;

Eileen Baber, Bill Backler, Nigel Bacon, Sandra Baer, Karl Bailey, Sheila Bailey, Christine Bainbridge, Mary Bainbridge, Samuel Baines, Sue Baines, Caroline Baird, Daphne Bairstow, Cherry Baker, Hannah Baker, Kate Baker, Mark Baker, R.E. Baker, James Baldwin, Caroline Ball, Damian Ballam, Nicola Ballard, Claire Bamber, A Bamford, Kunal Bandekar, John Bannister, Katie Bannister, Ashley Banyard, Nick Barber, Raymond Barclay, Paul Barfoot, Orsi Bark, Cherry Barker, June Barker, Russell Barker, Michael Barlow, Ruth Barlow, Stan Barlow, Susan Barlow, David Barnard, Judith Barnard, Cindy Barnes, Stephen Barnes, Reuben & Anna Baroni, Diane Barratt, Duncan Barratt, Cate Barrow, Christine Bartlett, Jo Barton, Sian Barton, Mary Barwell, Carole Bason, Natalie Bass, Adam Bassett, Elizabeth Bateman, Andrea Bates, Glenda Bates, Lena Bates, Rosemary Bates, Sheila Bates, Paul Batlow, G Batsman, Maureen Batt, Glen Batten, Gabrielle Battersby, David Battle, Christine Bauer, Geraldine Baxter, Jonathan Beacall, Chris Beach, Valerie Beadle, Ann Beaney, Craig Beard, Janet Beard, John Beard, Ginnie Beardmore, Jenni Beasley, Jaci Beaven, Elisabeth Beccle, June Beck, Petra Beck, Tina Beck, Megan Beckett, Tony Bedford, Carolyn Beech, A Beechey, Bernadette Beevor, Colin Begg, Alastair Behenna, Helen Belasco, Christine Bell, Colin Bell, Simon Bell, Peter Bellamy, Andy Benford, Colin Benford, James Benford, John Benford, M.J. Bennan, Drew Bennellick, Barbara Bennett, Caroline Bennett, David Bennett, Gavin Bennett, Lorraine Bennett, Nick Bennett, Dianne Benson, Rick Benson-Bunch, Hugh Bentley, Ashley Beolens, Fiona Beresford, Will Bermingham, Phil Bernard, Irmgard Berry, Matthew Berry, Ian Beswick, Ken & Brenda Betteridge, Christine Betts, Louis Bhavnani, Robina Bignell, Sara Billins, June Binns, Sara Binns, Christine Birch, Patsy Bishop, Lucy Bjorck, Rachel Black, Alison Blackborow, Peter Blackford, Simon Blackmore, James Blackwood, Julia Blake, Una Blake, Leia Blakesley, Greg Blanchard, Evelyn Blay, Gareth Blockley, Steve Blood, Eleanor Blott, Les Blundell, Norman Blundell, Jason Blunsdon, Carol Blyth, Jayesh Board, Nick Board, Paula Boddington, Jenny Bodkin, Harry Bold, Andrew Bolton, Margaret Bolton, Clare Bond, Josh Bond, Peter Bond, Judith Bone, Frances Bonner, Amy Bonner-Davies, Michael Bonsall, Alex Booker, Julia Booker, Anne Booth, Nikki Booth, Norain Booth, Peter Booth, Shelagh Borden, Amanda Borrows, Peter Borrows, Hannah Boschen, Amanda Bosley, Patrick Boston, Marc Botham, Chris Bottrell, Caroline Boudousquie, Anne Boughey, Martin Bourne, Naomi Bowen, Carole & Roy Bowler, Nick Bowles, Anna Bowman, Julie Bowser, Paul Bowyer, Helen Boyce, David Boyd, Nick Boyes, Samantha Boyes, Kate Bradbury, Betty Bradfield, Alfred Bradley, Lyndsay Brailsford, Michael Braithwaite, Jane & Peter Bramall, Lexi Bramall, Alan Brampton, Martin Brandom, Kirsty Brannan, Leslie Brant, Joanne Bray, Celia Brayfield, Ali Brazenor, Dorothy Brian, Barry Bricknell, George Bridge, Marilyn Bridges, Stuart Bridges, Penny Bridle, Clive Briffet, C B A Briggs, Jennifer Briggs, Lara Bright, Yvonne Brittan, Kathryn Brock, Phil Brock, Elizabeth Brodie, Kelly Brooker, Angela Brooks, Paul Broomhead, Anna Broszkiewicz, Kathy Broughton, Amanda Brown, Caroline Brown, Chris Brown, Daisy Brown, David Brown, Debra Brown, Derek Brown, Fiona Brown, Joanna Brown, Laura Brown, Lytton Brown, Stephanie Brown, Sue Brown, Val Brown, William Brown, Angela Brownrigg, Malcolm Brownsword, James Bruce, John Brucker, David Brunt, Debbie Brunton, Kim Bruty, Sarah Bryan, Georgina Buck, Adrian Buckel, Frances Buckel, Mike Buckland, Elizabeth Buckner-Rowley, James Buckridge, Jackie Buckton, Sam Buckton, Patricia Budd, Peter Bugg, Freddy Bull, John Bull, Keira Bull, Ricki Bull, Wayne Bull, Margaret Bulling, Ian Bullock, Janet Bullock, Jenny Bullock, Louise Bullock, Jenny Bulmer, Tracey Bulmer, Sue Bunker, Karen Bunn, Marie Bunting, Neville Burbeck, Brenda Burch, K Burchett, Anthea Burdess, Susan Burge, Luke Burgess, Jean Burley, Louis Burnard, Susan Burne, R Burness, Paulette Burns, Michael Burridge, Inge Burton, Paul Busby, Vanessa Busby, Phyl Butcher, Russell Butcher, Susan Butcher, Jan Butler, Kate Butler, Mary Butler, Sarah Buxton, Sue Buys, Luke Byca, Karen Byfield, Rosemary Byrde;

Jane Cadd, Jennie Cadd, Talia Cadd, Adrian Cadman, Louise Caesar, Lucy Cain, Sasha Cain, Sara Callen, Rachel Calver, Mark Calway, Hilary Campbell, J M Campbell, Jenny Campbell, Mick Campbell, Wendy Campbell, Irene Canning, Nicola Canning, Rebecca Canning, Richard Canning, Joyce Capey, Mollie Capey, Sue Cardiff, Ben Carpenter, Paul Carpenter, Sara Carpenter, Robin A Carr, Thalia Carr, Claire Carroll, Joan Carroll, Margaret Carruthers, Chris Carter, David Carter, Jenny Carter, Mary Carter, Steve Carter, Louis Cartledge, Jo Cartmell, Maggie Cartridge, Gillian Cartwright, Alison Casserly, Alan Cassidy, Gillian Cassidy, Valerie Castle, Gwen Castle-Payne, Eve Catlett, Anastasia Cauchi, Peter Cave, Tim Cave, Simon Chadbone, Calum Chalmers, Deborah Chalmers, Hayley Chalmers, Laura Chalmers, Kay Chamberlain, Emily Chambers, David Channing-Williams, Sheila Chantry, Hugh Chaplin, Debbie Chapman, Anna Charles, Peter Charles, Elaine Charlson, Christine Charlton, Ann Charnley, J Charter, Marie Anne Chattaway, Wendy Cheah, Karin Cheetham, Anthony Cheke, Nicola Chester, Patricia Chinnery, Flemming Christensen, Helen Christopher, Ann Chrzanowski, Eddie Church, Gi Clapton, Harvey Clare, B A J Clark, C L Clark, Jackie Clark, Natalie Clark, Rachael Clark, Ryan Clark, Steve Clark, Tim Clark, Tony Clark, Alan Clarke, Angela Clarke, Cathy Clarke, Eve & Sid Clarke, Julian H Clarke, Margaret Clarke, Nigel Clarke, Phil Clarke, Sue Clarke, Maria Clarkson, Sara Clavin, Andrew Claxton, Fam Clay, Ailsa Claybourn, Jake Claydon, Warren Claydon, Ian Clayton, Dave Cleal, David Cleal, Nigel Cleere, Brian Clews, B.J Clift, Patricia Clissold, M J Clist, Don Cload, Sue Cload, Gerald Clough, John Clough, Paul Clough, Isaac Clow-Jones, Vicki Clubley-Moore, Ian & Pearl Cochrane, Margaret Cochrane, Ann Cockerton, Jane Cockman, Peter Cockrell, Peter Cohen, Alan Cole, Lauren Cole, Sally Colegrove, Kevin Coleman, Phil Coles, Barry Collett, Jenny Collett, Anne J Collie, Adrian Collier, Justin Collier, Andy Collins, Christopher Collins, Julia Collins, Marilyn Collins, Perle Collins, Phillada Collins, Julia Collinson, Shelui Collinson, James Colson, Brian Colthorpe, Clair Colton, Janet Conabeer, Pamela Connell, Lesley Connolley, Judy Consden, Mike Consden, E M Cook, Hazel Cook, Mary Cook, Megan Cook, Sallie Cook, Sue Cook, Tim Cook, Corinne Cooke, David Cooke, Patricia Cooke, Helen Cookson, Beth Cooley, Barry Cooper, Christine Cooper, Gavin Cooper, Max Cooper, Natasha Cooper, Oliver Cooper, Ruth Cooper, Sarah Cooper, Kevin Copestake, Gillian Copperthwaite, Chris Coppock, A Corbett, Steven Cordery, Alison Cordiner, Dave Corfield, Martin & Alison Corley, Graham Cormack, Anna Corrie, Hannah Corrigan, Jennifer Costello, Peter Costigan, Peter Cotton, Gillian Coulson, Joe Coulson, Steve Coulson, Andrew Coupe, Meryl Course, Jonathan Court, Jan Cousins, Jane Coutanche, Rebecca Couzens, Jennie Covell, Nicki Cowley, Keith Cowton, Diane Cox, Geoff Cox, Linda Cox, Paul Cox, Sylvia Cox, Peter Cox-Smith, Frances Craig, Trevor Cramphorn, Dee Crane, Trevor Crane, Brian Crathorne, Claire Crawford, R Crawford, Anthony Crawforth, Vanessa Creech, Jani Crichton, Margaret Crick, Kirsten Crisford, Caroline Crisp, Vikki Critchley, Anthony Croft, Nicola Croft, T Croft, Tony Croft, Barbara Croker, Dick Croker, Sarah Crompton, Lindsey Cronin, Richard Crook, William Crook, Mrs W Cropper, P Cropper, Rosemary Cropper, Barbara Cross, Maureen Cross, Peter Cross, David Crossland, Jon Crouch, Sheila Crowson, Paul Crowther, Mary Crowther-Alwyn, Steve Croxford, Sue Croxford, Pat Crutch, Pauline Crutch, David Cullen, Andrew Culshaw, Carolyne Culver, Michelle Cunningham, Morgan Currant, Rob Curtis, Victoria Curtis, Wendy Curtis, Peter Cuss, Carole Cutcliffe, Rebecca Cutter;

Susan Daenke, Chris D'Agorne, Alice Daish, Cathy Daisy, Alison Dale, Jenny Dallinger, Peter Daltry, Keith Dancey, Laura Daniells, John Daniels, Maxine Daniels, Christine Danks, Michael Darby, Diane Darling, Fiona Dauppe, Louise Davidson, Ann Davies, Chris Davies, Haddon Davies, Howard Davies, Jean Davies, Karen Davies, Mary Davies, Robert Davies, Susie Davies, Christine Davis, Jennifer Davis, Nick Davis, Paul Davis, Sandra Davis, Susannah Davis, Bernard Davison, Tabitha Davison, Andrew Daw, John Daw, Brett Dawson, Jen Dawson, Lottie Day, Mark Day, Paul Day, Rosalind Day, Tim Day, Lucy de Albuquerque, Valerie de Burgh, Amelie de Chazal, Muriel de Grey, R de Kayser, Rien de Keyser, Moyna de Selincourt, Charlie Dean, Martin & Elaine Dear, Erica De'Ath, Lyn Deavin, Elizabeth Debenham, Russell Deer, Dennis Dell, John Dellow, Lorna Denby, Susan Denholm, Louise Denning, Charlotte Dennis, Chris Dennis, David Dennis, John Dennis, Pat Dennis, Richard Dennis, Sarah Dennis, Kate Dent, Mike Dent, Christine Depper, Alison Derrick, Sally Desbois, Joban Dey, Steven Dey, Colin Dibb, Sue Dickenson, Charles Dickerson, Abigail Dickson, Jo Dickson, Karen Dillamore, Anna Dillon, Barry Dinnage, Faith Disney, Desmond Dix, Chris Dixon, Esme Dixon, Tanya Dixon, Rhona Djaelani, Moira Dlugosz, Roger Dobbs, Roy Dobson, Bernard Dod, Martine Dodd, Matthew Dodds, Tessa Dodwell, Jane Doe, Hazel Dolling, Howard Dolling, Tony Dolton, Sally Dolz, Jeff Dominy, Bruce Don, Peter Donne, Alison Donnelly, Christine Donohue, Claire Dooley, Charlie Dormer, Peter Douch, Katie Doward, James Dower, Gail Dowlen, Marian Down, Stuart M Downhill, Louise Drakes, Penny Drew, Alastair Driver, Jen Drury, Robin Dryden, Michelle Dublon, Mark Duckworth, Emma Duffield, David & Marie Duffy, Elizabeth Dulston, Tom Dunbar, Helen Duncan, Kevin Duncan, Eric Dunford, Sheila Dunford, Roger Dunklin, Katy Dunn, Paul Durrands, Norman Dutton, Andrew Dyball, Michelle Dyke, Iain Dykes, Sam Dyson;

Kerry Earl, Diana Eastwood, Geoff Eaton, John Eborall, Sabine Eckert, John Edgar, Clive Edgson, Jackie Edington, Anna Edwards, Bob Edwards, Charlotte Edwards, George Edwards, J Edwards, John Edwards, Mollie Edwards, Mr & Mrs Julian Edwards, Neil Edwards, Neville Edwards, Paul Edwards, Zoe Edwards, Bob Eeles, Peter Eeles, Henry Eggleton, Pat Eisner, Paul Elborn, Bridget Elcombe, Graham Elcombe, Loren Eldred, Eleonora Eleonora, Mary Elford, Lee Ellams, Robert Elliott, Mr & Mrs A.C. Ellis, R Ellis, Richard Ellis, Bob Ellisdon, James Ellison, Nick Ellson, Vanessa Elphick, Richard Elston, Peter Elton, Dian Elvin, Tyrone Emery, Higgins Emma, Ann Engel, Susan Erskine, Ian Esland, Gemma Essex, Catalina Estrada, Alex Evans, Alison Evans, Charlotte Evans, Dawn Evans, Dick Evans, Gill Evans, Jane Evans, Jennifer Evans, Lee Evans, Nigel Evans, Ruth Evans, Sarah Evans, Stephen Evans, Tom Evans, Barbara Evans Rees, Colin Everett, Pauline Everett, Gaelle Evrard, Jo Exell;

Penny Fabien, Fiona Fahy, Elliott Fairs, Simon Falconer, Steven Falk, Ann Falkner, Noogle Fallon, Stephen Farmer, S J Farnsworth, Charles Farrell, Dave Farren, Alma Faulkner, Steph Fawdry, David Fearn, Kathleen Fearn, Michael Featherbe-Knott, Vanessa Fell, Sian Fellers, Mark Fellowes, Nick Felstead, Ann Feltham, Revelyne Fenner, Una Fenton, Becky Ferguson, Dave Ferguson, Gisela Ferguson, Kay Ferguson, Lukas Ferguson, Ruth Ferrara, Geoff Ferrari, Simon Ferris, Abby Fettes, Richard Ffrench-Constant, Anna Field, Michael Field, Tony Filbee, Benjamin Filer, L J Finch, M J Finch, Graham Firth, Michelle Fisher, Brian Fitton, Jacqueline Fitzmaurice, David Flack, Keith Fleming, Neil Fletcher, Claire Flint, Jim Flint, Jacqui Flisher, Cynthia Floud, Ursula Flowers, Susan Foden, Margaret Foley, Sandy Folliard, Sheila Fooks, Stephen Foot, Adrian Ford, Ella Ford, J Ford, Lesley Ford, Richard Forrest, Miranda Forrester, Jayne Forsyth, Peter Foskett, Susan Fossey, Andrew Foster, Chris Foster, Linda Foster, Peta Foster, Debby Fox, Oliver Fox, Richard Fox, Rosemary Fox, Karen Foxall, Phil Foxan, Keith Francis, Tamara Franklin, Roger Frankum, Christine Fraser, Anne Freeman, Jo Freeman, Steve Freeman, G.S. Freemantle, John Freemantle, Suzanne French, Katherine Frend, Yvonne Frewin, Ben Frost, Sandra Frost, Robert Fryer, Charlotte Fulford, David Fuller, Maddy Fulton, Phil Furneaux, Margaret Furniss, Nick Furtek, Paul Furtek;

Karen Gaches, Janet Gaines, Linda Gale, Derek Gallagher, Paul Gallagher, Ian Gamble, Kaye Gambles, Mrs J Gammon, Johan Gant, Rod Gant, David Gantzel, Bob Gardner, Carol Gardner, Dawn Garlick, Cheryl Garner, Clo Garner, Kelly Garnham, Kat Garrow, Lloyd Garvey, Sophie Gaskell, Lucian Gaudoin, Mette Gauguin, Linda Gaull, Geraldine Gault, Buena Gauron, Cara Gauron, Phil Gauron, John Gearing, Sue Gedney, Jacqui Gee, Ched George, Helen George, Lois George, Neil George, Joyce Gibbard, John Gibbings, Emma Gibbons, Colin Gibbs, Jamie Gibbs, Patricia Gibson, Sylvia Gibson, Len Gilchrist, E Gilkerson, Andrew Gill, Marion Gill, Neil Gill, Sandy Gill, Susan Gill, Ralph Gillam, Glenys Gillespie, Gray Gillian, Janet Gillie, Marion Gillie, Tony Gillie, Elaine Gillies, Richard Gillies, Anstace Gladstone, Janet Gladstone, David Gleave, Christopher Gleeson, Catherine Gleghorn, Max & William Glencairn-Campbell, Georgina Glenny, Clive Glover, Rebecca Goddard, Steve Goddard, Robert Godden, Valerie Godfrey, Nicola Golding, Richard Golding, Roger Golding, Suzanne Golinski, Alison Gomm, Francis Gomme, Ellie Good, Tracy Gooding, Sue Goodman, Mary Goodrum, Gill Goodwin, Tim Goodwin, Liz Goodyear, Zena Gordon, Mel Gordon-Moore, Anthony Gore, Rachel Gormley, Diana Gorton, Jason Gosling, Helen Gould, John Gould, Sarah Gould, David Gower, Sue Gower, Nigel Gowing, Andrew Graham, Deirdre Graham, Robert Graham, Tim Graham, Ian Grainger, Alexia Granatt, John Grandidge, Deborah Grant, Margaret Grant, Caroline Graty, Chris Gravell, Hannah Graves, Kathryn Graves, Chris Gray, David Gray, Gillian Gray, Sally Gray, Renee Grayer, Annette Greathead, Adrian Green, E E Green, Jeremy Green, Kate Green, Kelly Green, Kim Green, Roy Green, Sue Green, Ted Green, D Greenaway, Jane Greengrass, Alison Greenhalh, Katy Greenwood, Anne Gregory, Irene Gregory, Rita Gregory, Jenny Grewal, Charlie Grieve, Graeme Griffin, Maya Griffith, Robert Griffith, Chris Griffiths, Elinor Griffiths, Freya Griffiths, Helen Griffiths, Mark Griffiths, Donald Grigg, Hilary Grime, Anne Grimm, Jessie Grimond, Inger Grindley, John Gripper, Jane Grisdale, Angela Grist, Sandra Grist, Gloria Grove, Justin Groves, Jennie Grubb, Lisa Gubby, Alan Gudge, Juliet Gudge, Muriel Gudgin, Celia Gulland, Melissa Gundem, Marie Alice Gurr, Jeremy Gurton;

Susan Hadfield, Gavin Hageman, Barbara Hahn, Jackie Haines, Keith Hainge, Avril Hale, Angie Hales, Hermione Hales-Owen, Julie Halford, Chloe Hall, Christopher Hall, Elisabeth Hall, Hazell & Tony Hall, Jennifer Hall, Pam Hall, Ros Hallett, Jo Hamer, Sara Hamilton, Miranda Hamish-Wilson, Louise Hammond, Janice Hammons, David Hanchet, Christine Hancock, Shelley Hancock, Jo Handford, John Hanratty, Roy Hansford, Elizabeth Hanson, James Happs, Trecia Harden, Anthony Harding, Richard Harding, Clare Hardy, Mike Hardy, Nick Hardy, Peter B Hardy, Rebecca Harker, Paul Harley, Shelagh Harlow, Tony W Harman, Jim Harper, Shay Harper, Jameson Harriet, Alan Harrington, Richard Harrington, Bess Harris, Caroline Harris, Cathy Harris, Emily Harris, Joe Harris, John Harris, Niki Harris, Carina Harrison, Kirsty Harrison, Robert Harrison, Cecil Harrold, Sheila Harry, Celia Hart, Richard Hart, Lola Harter, Adam Hartley, Linda Hartlih, Clare Harvey, David Harvey, Dominic S Harvey, Ed Harvey, Helen Harvey, Martin Harvey, Mrs A Harvey, Claire Haseler, Jan Haseler, Laurie Haseler, Jo Hassall, David Hassell, Peter Hassett, David Hastings, Donna Hathaway, Sarah Hatton, Grahame Hawker, Lesley Hawker, Marion Hawkesworth, Andrew Hawkins, David Hawkins, Wendy Hawkins, Dianne Haworth, Stephen Hayden, Gillian Hayers, Alex Hayes, Betty Hayes, Kate Hayes, Penny Hayes, Shawndra Hayes-Budgen, Julia Hayford, Derek G Haynes, Janie Haynes-Ager, Paul Hayter, F Hayward, Jemma Hayward, Paul Hayward, Sue Hayward, Chris Hazell, Christina Hazlewood, Tim Hearn, Fiona Hedicker, Elizabeth Heike, Rosemary Held, Jean Helm, Elizabeth Helsby, Anna Hemmings, John Hemmings, Jean Henderson, Sue Hendrie, Tessa Hennessy, James Herd, Estelle Herszenhorn, Susan Hewett, Lynda Hewitson, R Hewitt, Liz Hibberdine, Andy Hickman, Peter Hickman, Richard Hicks, Victoria Hicks, Tom Higevold, Jennifer Higginson, Tony Higgott, Matthew Higgs, Valerie Higgs, Stephanie Higham, Rosemary Hignett, S Hiknet, Alex Hill, Alison Hill, Elizabeth Hill, Graham Hill, John Hill, Lynne Hill, Rob Hill, Simon Hill, Sophi Hill, Tracey Hill, Clare Hilary, Maisy Hillier, Peter Hills, Eddie Hing, Brian Hinson, Philip Hinton, Andrew Hirst, Gerry Hiscock, Jane Hiscock, Liz Hiscock, Susan Hiscock, Caroline Hitch, James Hitchcock, Jacqui Hitt, Katy Hoad, A M Hoare, D J Hoare, Dan Hoare, Ben Hobbs, Margaret Hobson, John Hockey, D.G. Hodge, Linda Hodges, Stuart Hodges, Jenny Hodgkinson, Tina Hoffmann, Jennifer Hogan, Freya Hogevold, Penny Hogevold, Thomas Hogevold, Tom Hogevold, Annie Hogg, John Holdbrook, John Holder, Charles Hole, Stella Hole, Ruth Holland, Gill Holliday, Steve Holliday, Michael Hollis, Alison Holloway, Neil Holman, Justine Holt, Norma Holt, Rosemary Holt, Rowena Holt, Tim Holt, Patsy Hook, Caroline Hooper, David Hooper, Peter Hooper, Angela Hope-Murray, Teresa Hopkins, Julia Hopkinson, Gloria Hopkins-Smith, Christopher Hopper, Ed Hopper, Carol Hopperton, Cedric Hoptroff, Margaret Horne, Tim Horwood, Andy Hoskins, Christine Hoskins, Rodney Houghton, John Houlihan, Isabella House, Daniel Howard, Danny Howard, Denise Howarth, David Howdon, Brian Howe, Julian Howe, Nicholas Howell, Frances Howells, Heather Howes, Lucie Howes, Jan Howlett, Monica Howlett, Petra Hoyer Millar, Douglas Hoyle, Paul Huckle, Terence Huckle, Gill Hudson, Maria Hudson, Tim Hufford, Isobel Huggins, Julia Huggins, Richard Huggins, Saskya Huggins, Carol Hughes, David Hughes, Frances Hughes, Gareth Hughes, Joy Hughes, Pamela Hughes, Steve Hughes, Beryl Hulbert, Joe Humm, Derek & Janet Humphries, Joe Hunt, Joy Hunt, Lizzie Hunt, Michael Hunt, Nikita Hunt, Steve Hunt, Vicky Hunt, Liz Hunter, Sue Hunter, Jonathan Hurley, Barbara Hurman, Lee Hurrell, Harry Hurst, Charles Hussey, Nancy Hussey, Trevor Hussey, Margaret Hutchings, Gillian Hutchinson, Jane Hutchinson, Stephanie Hutchison, Kenneth Huxham, Helen Hyre, Nigel Hyre;

Ruth Ibbotson, Chris Iles, Sara Iles, John Illenden, Viv Illingworth, Emma Ing, David & Elizabeth Ingledew, Hilary Ingold, Linda Inness, Nicola Iqbal, Sally & Dave Irven, Anne Irvine, Richard Irvine;

Anne Jackson, Auriol Jackson, Barry Jackson, Charlie Jackson, Kaye Jackson, Robert Jackson, Nick Jacobsen, Warren Jacques, Brian James, Catherine

James, Elizabeth James, Emma James, Fiona James, Freddie James, Jackie James, Mark James, Nick James, Richard James, Sheila James, Barry Jameson, Nick Jamieson, Keith Janes, Richard Jarman, Fiona Jefferson, Victoria Jefferson, Rosemary Jeffery, Peter Jeffs, Ellie Jenkins, Hilary Jenkins, Rebecca Jenkins, Stuart Jenkins, Marilyn Jennings, Ruth Jennings-Day, Isaac Jervis, Brian Jessop, Sarah Jewer, Joanna Joanna, Donna Joans, Joy Johns, Brian Johnson, Debs Johnson, Wendy Johnson, Colin Johnstone, Michael Jolley, Katie Jolly, Alan Jones, Alleyne Jones, Bernadette Jones, Ian Jones, Imogen Jones, Jeremy Jones, Kate Jones, Kerry Jones, Lesley Jones, Melvyn Jones, Mick Jones, Mrs H R Jones, Patricia Jones, Pauline Jones, Philip Jones, Sally Jones, Sandie Jones, Stephen Jones, Shyla Jordan, Richard Josephy, R Josey, Josiejo Josiejo, Jos Joslin, Astrid Jowett, Angie Julian;

Veronica Kaenzig, Deborah Kaplinsky, Saxl Karen, Rhonda Karpenic, David Kay, Quinn Kay, Rob Keel, Alison Keen, Eleanor Keen, Sharon Keen, Janet Keene, Beryl Kellow, Ian Kelloway, Caroline Kelly, Dan Kelly, Jean Kelly, Lisa Kelly, Liz Kelly, Jenny Kelsey, Rosemary Kember, Martin Kemp, Roger Kemp, Mike Kempton, Gerry Kendall, Penny Kendall, Anne Kennedy, Doug Kennedy, Anna Kenny, Iain Kent, Kerry Kent, Hannah Kenyon, Ruth Kenyon, I.M. Kerr, June Kersten, Christine Kestell-Cornish, Martin Kettell, Margaret Kevern, Charlie Kew, Michelle Kewfi, Lorraine Khan, Mary Khawaja, Stella Khenia, Gordon Kidd, Tina Kikaj, Dave Kilbey, Mike Killeby, Neil Killoran, Sue & Neil Killoran, Sandra Kimber, Martin Kincaid, Phillip M Kinder, Andy King, Chris King, Esther King, Isabel King, Neil King, Philippa King, Sandra King, Sue King, Rowena Kingston, Katie Kinnaird, Melvyn Kirby, Alex Kirkman, Michal Klafkowski, Bhupinder Klair, Bob Knight, Judith Knight, Sarah Knowles, John Knox, Helena Korjonen, Julian Korn, Krysia Krysia, Adam Kwolek;

Katie Lacy, Christa Laird, Annie Laister, John Laker, Joks Laker, Felix Lam, Colin & Lynne Lambert, Jane Lambert, Audrie Lambourne, Jill Lampier, Chris Lamsdell, Janet Lancaster, Emma Lane, Viki Lane, Kerry Lapworth, Sarah Larkin-Smith, Joanna Larmour, Elizabeth Laskar, Gillian Last, Pamela Laughton, Tony Lavers, David Law, Peter Law, Roger Law, Mike Lawrence, Adrian Lawson, Andrew Lawson, Caroline Layton, Delphine Le Pevelen, Bryan Lea, David Learoyd, Thomas Learoyd, Deanna Lecoyte, Alex Ledger, Ellen Lee, Eloise Lee, Trish Lee, Susan Lee-Tanner, Jan Legg, Karl Lehmann, John Lerpiniere, Chris Leslie, Jan Lesser, Christine Lester, Beulah Letchford, Jenny Letts, Daphne Lever, Sara Levick, Juliet Levy, Christine Lewin, Susanne Lewington, Maddy Lewis, Mark Lewis, Owen Lewis, Scarlett Lewis, Suzanne Lewis Woodley, Karen Leydon, Gillian Liddell, Karen Lillywhite, Kate Limburn, Graham Lincoln, John Lindley, Christopher Lindsay, Pat Lingane, Sarah Lingham, Dick Lister, Toby Lister, M.J. Litchfield, Kate Little, Margaret Little, Helen Liversidge, Michelle Livett, Fiona Livingstone, Alex Lloyd, Heidi Lloyd, Matthew Lloyd, Pam Lloyd, Pat Lloyd, Sarah Lloyd, John Lloyd Parry, Sian Lloyd-Pennell, David Lloyd-Williams, John Loader, Steve Lockey, Rachel Locklin, Susan Logan, Graham Long, John Long, Steve Long, Liz Lonsdale, Patricia Lonsdale, Orysia Love, Elaine Lovell, Nicholas Low, Alison Lowe, Helen Lowe, Heather Lowther, Andy Lucas, Hazel Lucas, P Lucas, Alice Luck, Gill Lucraft, Carolyn Luff, Belinda Lugg, Erica Lugg, Andy Lumbard, Robert Lumley, C Lumsdell, Paul Lund, Tim Lunel, Catherine Lunn, Marie Lunnon, Jan Lunsford, Niall Lusby, James Lyall, Alexandra Lyes, John Lynam, Lynne Lynne, Patrick Lytton Brown;

Callum Macgregor, Lisa Macgregor, Neil Macgregor, Anne Mack, Dominic Mackenzie, Elizabeth Mackey, Hannah Mackie, Mel Mackie, Anna Mackin, Andrew Maclellan, Evelyn Macmillan, John Magee, Mike Magee, Martin Maguire, J Main, Janet Main, Nicki Main, Peter Mainwaring, Ellie Makri, Family Malabon, John Mander, Darren Mann, Janet Manning, Audrey Mansfield, Carol Mansfield, Mark Mansfield, Peter Mansfield, Susan Manston, Lucy Manwaring, Alun March, Georgia Marchington, Tricia Marcouse, Roxane Marffy, Michelle Margot, Helen Maric, T Marlow, Donna Marriott, Ruth Marriott, Garry Marsh, Richard Marsh, Tony Marsh, Alan Marshall, Alison Marshall, Richard Marshall, Rosemary Marshall, Susan Marshall, Trish Marshall, Derek Martin, Fiona Martin, Louise Martin, Paul Martin, Daniel Mason, Emily Mason, Joanna Mason, Keith Mason, Margaret Mason, Elaine Matejtschuk, Colin Mather, Shirley Mather, Lynn Mathieson, Dave Mattam, Brenda Matthews, Carol Matthews, Nicholas Matthews, Vanessa Matthews, Izzy Mattick, Tony Mattingley, Max Maughan, David Maunder, Terry Mawdesley, Chris Mawson, Clair Maxwell, Maria Maxworthy, Carole May, Matt May, Matt May, Carol Mayes, Trish Mayler, D Maynard, Peter Maynard, Graham Mays, Jessie Mcauley, Natalie Mccarthy, Roy Mccawley, Sue Mcclaughry, Buffy McClelland, Gwen McConnachie, Lynette Mcconnell, Ruth Mccracken, Kate Mcdonald, Rob Mcdonald, Catherine McEwan, Sarah Mcewan, Derek Mcewen, Melanie Mcfadden, Janet Mcgarvey, Dee Mcgivney, Graham Mcgowan-Smyth, Susanne Mcinnes, Brendan Mckenna, Kathryn Mckenzie, Alistair Mckinnon, Duncan Mclean, Wendy Mclean, Penny Mcleish, Brian Mclelland, Keith McMahon, Linnet Mcmahon, Maxine Mcmahon-Brown, Derek Mcmanus, Neil Mcmillan, Michael McNeill, Callum Mcpherson, Cath Mcpherson, Alan Mcquitty, Katie Mctavish, Torin Mcvean, Kathy Mead, Pat Mead, Vivienne Mead, David Meadows, Colin Meager, Wendy Meagher, Cheryl Meaning, Judiths Mears, John Melling, Rob Mellon, Hugh Mellor, Mary Melluish, Christine Melton, David Melzack, Beatrice Mercer, Janet Mercer, Edward Mercer-Gray, Joely Mercer-Gray, Saskia Mercer-Gray, Thomas Merckx, Ken & Rita Merrifield, Richard Merritt, Aaron Merry, Lotte Meteyard, Metski Metski, Alison Michael, Jonathan Middlemiss, Dick Middleton, Jackie Middleton, Reed Mike, Sandie Milam, D Millar, Ian Millard, John Millard, B. Miller, Ben Miller, Caitlin Miller, Dave Miller, Douglas Miller, John Miller, Lynne Miller, Penny Miller, Ian Miller-Hall, Carolyn Millikin, Doreen Mills, Leigh Milsom, Maureen Milsom, Jane Milton, Joanne Milton, Coral Mist, Joel Mitchell, Martin Mitchell, Sharon Mitchell, Zoe Mitchell, Nadine Mitschunas, Brenda Mobbs, Mike Mobbs, G Moffatt, M J Moffatt, Ro Mogridge, Ta Mole, Jan Molin, Jane Mollison, Simon Mollison, Nick Monaghan, Jackie Moncur, Jim Monger, Jones Monica, Judith Mooney, Heather Moore, Kayleigh Moore, Tony Moore, Mike Morecroft, Gwyneth Morgan, Huw Morgan, Finn Morgans, Dave Morris, E.P. Morris, Steve Morris, Bronwyn Morrison, Malcolm Mortimer, Trevor Mortimer, Alan J Morton, Hilary Morton, Sue Morton, Linda Moses, Charlotte Moss, Paula Moss, Iona Mountain, Carol Mowat, Sarah Muddell, John Mullaney, Jilly Muller, David Mullins, Lina Mulrenan, Caroline Munro, Cindy Munro, Tapashya Murali, Emma Murphy, Linda Murphy, Sean Murphy, Steve Murphy, Jack & Finley Murray, Justine Murrin, Mike Muston, Janice Myburgh, Alison Myers, Claire Myers, Derek Myers, Bernadette Mynes, Toby Mynott, Alison Myres;

Claire Naden, Chris Naish, Alison Napier, Cynthia Napper, Eddie Napper, Alan Nash, Amelia Nash, Joan Nassim, Rachael Naylon, Edward Neal, Stephanie Neal, Debra Needham, Kate Neill, June Nelson, Sian New, Linda Newbery, Maria Newham, Beryl Newman, Isabelle Newman, Roger Newman, S Newman, Sue Newman-Crane, Toni Newnham, Terence Newsome, Josephine Newton, Stella Newton, Jan Nicholas, Sheila Nicholas, Elaine Nicholson, Thomas Nicol, Oliver Nixon, Fiona Noble, Richard Noble, Kathryn Noon, Philip Noon, Tommy Norcup, Chris Norman, Carol Norris, Barbara North, Nicky Northam, Roger Norton, Aidrian Nowell, Saskia Nowell, Angela Noy, Helen Nunn, Michelle Nunn;

Karen Oakes, Clare Oakley, Val Oakley, Mark Oates, Matthew Oates, Garry O'Brien, Maggie O'Brien, Gerald O'Connell, Mick O'Connor, Caroline Oden, Andrew O'Driscoll, Peter Ogden, Keith O'Hagen, John O'Keeffe, Gillian Oldfield, Celia Oldham, J Oliver, Laura Oliver, Nick Oliver, Trish Oliver, Crispin Oram, Elizabeth Oram, Anna Oreszczyn, Giles Orpen, Mrs M A Osborn, Rosemary Osborne, Dorothea O'Shea, Val Osmond, Ruby Osorio, V T O'Sullivan, Ewan Otten, Don Otter, Hilary Oulton, David Ouvry, Michael Overend, Mark Overton, Jenny Owen, Lewis Owen, Anne Oxley;

Jean Packer, Claire Packham, Steve Padget, Andrew Padmore, Jennie Page, Rachel Page, Anne Pagett, Susan Paice, Marcus Pakes, Jeremy Palmer, Michelle Palmer, Pippa Palmer, Stephanie Palmer, Michal Parak, Ade Parker, Bill Parker, Janet Parker, Julie Parker, Louise Parker, Rick Parker, Su Parker, Richard Parkes, Luke Parkin, Josephine Parkinson, Valerie Parkinson, Dave Parmenter, A.D. Parr, Doug Parr, J Parsons, Nigel Parsons, Sue Parsons, Tim Parsons, Nigel Partridge, Rhiannon Partridge, J Pascoe, Frances Passey, Dinesh Patel, Kat Patrick, Roger Paul, Gael Paulsson, Shari Pay, Andree Payne, Chris Payne, Mary Payne, Sophie Payne, Holly Payton, Malcolm Peake, Joel Pearce, Rob Pearce, Vicky Pearce, Victoria Pearce, Andrea Pearn, Anna Pearson, Jennifer Pearson, Mark Pearson, Nicky Pearson, Jo Peck, Jonathan Peck, Helen Pedder, Jack Peeters, Marian Pell, Delphine Penfold, Isabella Penfold, Lynn Penfold, Carlton Penn, Ruth Penn, Phil Penson, Nick Percival, Rupert Perkins, Sylvia Perks, Debbie Perry, Philippa Perry, Alison Peters, Gregory Peters, Jack Peters, Paula Peters, Rachel Peters, Sue Peters, Sarah Pethybridge, Robert Petts, Jodey Peyton, Claire Phillips, Clive Phillips, Hazel Phillips, Hilary Phillips, Kirstie Phillips, Sara Phillips, Suzanne Phillips, Timothy & Janet Phillips, Martin Phipps, Marc Phuket, David Pickering, Ed Pickering, Chris Pickford, Stephen Pickles, Candy Piercy, Jenny Pillar, Steve Piltz, Rebecca Pinkney, Neill Pitcher, Michael Pitt-Payne, Pauline Plampin, Stephanie Plaster, Joanna Plumb, Stephanie Plumb, Theo Pluto, Chris Poad, Michael Pocock, Jakub Polanski, Andrea Polden, Gail Pollard, Terry Pollard, Brian Pollinger, Bob Pomfret, Joy Pomfret, Elena Pond, Liz Pond, Lisa Popa, John Popple, James Port, Kim Potter, Richard Potter, Sarah Potter, David Pottinger, Lynn Potts, Andrea Powell, Annette Powell, Averil Powell, Elaine Powell, L Powell, Nicola Powell, Tony Powell, R Pratley, Ian Pratt, Mike Prentice, Nicky Prentice, Jean Prest, Ann Preston, Raymond Preston, Bernard Price, Felicity Price, Jacqui Price, Margaret Price, Roger Price, Beverly Priddle, Christopher Prideaux, Tim Primett, Tom Primett, Mandy Primmer, Michael Pritchard, Mike Pritchard, Diana Procter, Catharine Pschenyckyj, David Pugh, Inez Marina Pugh, Lyn Pugsley, Jacqueline Pumphrey, Gill Purchase, Sylvia Purkis, Sandra Purrett, Jan Pursall, Michael Pursglove, Barrie Puttock;

Dan Radusin, Anton Rae, Rosy Raines, Paul Rainsden, Amanda Ralfe, Marion Ralson, Chloe Rance, Kathleen Randall, Athena Randle, Chris Raper, D Raper, Louise Raper, Martin Raper, Krisha Rathod, Florence Raworth, Tony Rayner, Lorna Rea, Helen Read, Paul Reading, Reading and District Natural History Society, C Redfern, D Redhead, David Redhead, Wendy Redhead, Scarlett Redmond, Alan Reed, Mike Reed, Graham Reeve, Janet Reeve, Alan Reeves,

Alyssa Reeves, Elizabeth Reeves, John Reeves, Sophie Reeves, Carol Regulski, Maisie Reid, Mark Reid, Susan Reilly, Alice Renaud, Anna Renton-Green, Andy Reynolds, Debbie Reynolds, Jemima Reynolds, Michael Reynolds, Pamela Reynolds, Samuel Reynolds, Marcus Rhodes, Ben Richards, Hazel Richards, Lily Richards, Sara Richards, Ben Richardson, Katie Richardson, Malcolm Richardson, Martyn Richardson, Jim Richie, Charles Richmond, Colin Richmond, David Rickeard, Cara Rickett, Jake Ridd, Lucy Ridding, Paul Ridley, Michael Riggall, Adrian Riley, Jillian Riley, John Rissbrook, Anne Roberts, Barry Roberts, Gabriel Roberts, Karen Roberts, Mark Roberts, Gretta Robertson, Janice Robertson, Mike Robey, Sarah Robin, Amber Robinson, Belinda Robinson, Clifford Robinson, Emma Robinson, Kel Robinson, Laura Robinson, Martin Robinson, Michael Robinson, Oliver Robinson, Richard Robinson, Stella Robinson, Stephen Robinson, Susan Robinson, Tracey Robinson, Vicky Robinson, Charlotte Robson, Kit Robson, Victoria Rockell, Nora Rockenbauer-Edmonds, Robi Rockenbauer-Edmonds, Mandy Rodway, Derek Roe, Jenny Rogers, Marie Rollison, June Romans, Louise Ronan, Michael Root, Alex Roscoe, Edna Roscoe, Deborah Rosenthal, Alison Ross, David Ross, Helena Ross, James Ross, Mark Rossell, Carol Roth, Peter Rouse, Catherine Rowan Jones, Amy Rowe-Williams, Martin Rowland, Benjamin Rowley, David Roy, Helen Roy, Prem Roy, Catherine Rubinstein, Jane Rudd, Kate Rudd, Kathryn Rudd, Robert Rudge, Judith Rudham, Hazel Ruers, Teresa Rumble, Tom Rupniak, C Rush, Steven Rushworth, Ann Russell, Gina Russell, Inigo Russell, Jeremy Russell, Louise Russell, Rob Ryan, Tracey Ryan, Geoff Ryder, Catherine Rye, Vanessa Rye;

Penny Sackett, Kate Sadler, Forooz Saedi, Laraine Saedi, Peter Sage, Margaret Sahin, George Salethorne, Surinder Sall, Ben Salmon, Seiter Samantha, Claire Sampson, Mervyn Samuel, Rob Sandercock, Anne Sanders, Gillian Sandford, Christopher Sandham, Caroline Sandland, Roy Sargent, Caroline Sarton, John Saunders, Tony Savage, Karen Saxl, C Sayers, Denise Sayles, Ian Scarlett, Deborah Scattergood James, Christine Scaysbrook, Karen Schofield, Lisa Schofield, Graham Scholey, Karsten Schonrogge, Ethan Schrecker, Rose Scoones, Andrew Scotland, Jez Scott, Victor Scott, Rebecca Scrivens, Les Scriver, Stan Sear, Lesley Searle, Janet Seaton, Tia Sedley, Gretchen Seiffert, Paul Seligman, Charlotte Serpell, Hanna Setterahamne, Jenni Shafe, Nicola Shaffer, Renee Shah, John Sharp, Adela Sharpe, Lynne Sharpe, Marguerite Shave, Paul Shave, Bex Shaw, John Shaw, Marion Shaw, Rob Shaw, Ruth Shaw, S Sheikh, Phillipa Sheldrake, John Shelton, Christine Shepherd, Emma Shepherd, Mark Shepley, Rupert Sheppard, Linda Shepstone, Mike Sheridan, Carol Sherlock, Carole Sherwood, Ewan Shilland, Carol Shipton, Irene Short, John Shortland, Alan Showler, Valerie Siddiqui, Helen Simmonds, Pam Simmonds, Gregor Simmons, Janet Simmons, Carol Simms, Maggie Simons, Dennis Simpkin, Lisa Simpkin, Pamela Simpkins, Charles Simpson, Claire Simpson, Helen Simpson, Lynette Simpson, Sally Simpson, Clive Sims, Peter Skelton, Beryl Skinner, Oliver Sladen, Janet Slatter, Margery Slatter, Bren Sleight, Keith Sleight, Sue Smallbone, Daphne Smart, Oliver Smart, Rachel Smart, Patsy Smiles, Adrian Smith, Alex Smith, Alison Smith, Arthur Smith, Barbara Smith, Barnaby Smith, Bobby Smith, Danielle Smith, Davena Smith, Edwina Smith, Emily Smith, Heather Smith, Helen Smith, John Smith, Maureen Smith, Mike Smith, Mrs W.E. Smith, Nicola Smith, Paul Smith, Rachel Smith, Richard Smith, Rob Smith, Stuart Smith, Terrence Smith, Philip Smithson, Melanie Smythe, Jenny Sneddon, Emma Snell, Jeremy Soane, Liz Softley, Susan Sogunro, Wolf Solent, Sophie Soliman, David Soper, Richard Soulsby, Joan South, Lynda South, Judith Sowden, Jez Spearman, Tony Speight, Tony Speight, Barbara Spence, George Spence, Oliver Spence, Sally-Ann Spence, Helen Spencer, Ian Spencer, Jennifer Spencer, Robert Spencer, Shirley Spencer, Clive Spinage, Maria Spink, Paul Spinks, Andrew Spragg, Maggie Sproule, Pat Spurway, Gerald Stacey, John Stacey, Sarah-Jane Stacey, Christine Stainthorpe, Joanna Staley, Rob Stallard, Kevin & Sandra Stanbridge, Nick Standing, E Standley, Geoffrey Stanfield, Glyn Stanley, Julia Stanley, R Stansfield, Alfie Stanton, Vivienne Stanton, Jill Stanton-Huxton, Burt Staunton-Lamb, Stanley Staunton-Lamb, Emma Steed, Caroline Steel, Gaby Steel, Andrew Steele, Marie Steele, Liz Stephens, Carol Steppings, Alice Stevens, J Stevens, Paul Stevens, Victoria Stevens, J Stevenson, Thomas Stevenson, Tom Stevenson, Michelle Still, Ruth Stockland, N Stone, Pierre Storck, Robert Stothard, Ashley Stow, Adrian Stowell, Penny Stowell, Mark Stratton, Elizabeth Streatfeild, Emma Street, Sandra Street, Sarah Street, Elizabeth Streeter, Judi Stretton, Jolyon Stringer, Niki Stroud, Wendy Stroud, Ray Strugnell, Colin Stubberfield, Jenny Stubberfield, Duncan Stubbs, Richard Stubbs, Pauline Studman, Pam Styles, Lyndsay Suchodolski, Anthony Sulman, Graham Sumner, John Sumpter, Geraldine Surman, James Surman, Amelia Surrey, Des Sussex, Joanne Sutherland, Claire Sutton, Andrew Swann, Niamh Swatton, Nina R Sweet, Richard Swift, Roderick Swift, Emma Swingle, Helen Swinnerton, Ingrid Sylvester, Roderick Symonds, Sheila Syrad, Chris Szala;

Clare Talbot, Ruth Talbot, Thurston Tallack, Ian Tankard, Amoret Tanner, Lynn Targett, Susannah Tarlton, Kenneth Tarrant, Adam Taylor, Andrew Taylor, Gillian Taylor, Graham Taylor, Ian Taylor, Jo Taylor, Joshua Taylor, Julie Taylor, Lauren Taylor, Mandy Taylor, Martin Taylor, Max Taylor, Michael J Taylor, Michele Taylor, Moira Taylor, N Taylor, Simon Taylor, Suzanne Taylor, Vivienne Taylor, Philip Tearle, Carole Tebb, Jodie Telfer, Mark G Telfer, Ros Templeman, M Templeton, Amanda Terry, Michael Terry, K.J. Thacker, Ruth Thatcher, Barbara Thomas, Claire Thomas, Hannah Thomas, Helen Thomas, Jane Thomas, Marian Thomas, Penny Thomas, Rachel Thomas, Ron Thomas, Colin Thompson, Holly Thompson, Pam Thompson, Pete Thompson, Theresa Thompson, David Thomson, Lynn Thomson, Sarah Thomson, Brett Thorn, Chris Thorne, Simon Thorpe, Jan Thurley, Hollie Thynne, Hazel Tibbetts, Liz Tidy, Samantha Timms, Paul Tinworth, Kate Titford, Phil Tizzard, Julia Todd, Sheila Todd, Izzy Tollerfield, Megan Tollerfield, Maxine Tolson, Andy Tomczynski, Elizabeth Tomkinson, Lucy Tomkinson, Duncan Tomlinson, Mandy Tomlinson, Su Towler, Roger Townend, Tony Towner, Paul Townley, C Townsend, Paul Townsend, Tanya Tracey, P M Treadgold, Toby Trebert, Ian Tregaskis, Suzanne Tremmel, Stephen Trigg, Field Trip, Sean Tuck, Arnold Tucker, Rachel Tucker, Jackie Tuckey, Stephen Tuddenham, W R Tunnicliffe, Graham Tunstall, Michael Turff, David Turnbull, Emma Turnbull, Esther Turnbull, A Turner, David Turner, Fiona Turner, Janet Turner, Jo Turner, Lesley Turner, Roy Turner, Shirley Turner, B. Turtle, Mike Turton, Vanda Tuszynski, Susan Twigg, Peter Tyler, Chris Tyler-Smith, Joan Tyrrell;

Hilary Unwin, Amy Upton, Jon Uren, Ewan Urquhart, B Uttley;

Jenny Vale, Elizabeth Valentine, Mark Vallance, Mark Vaughan, Peggy Verrall, Petra Vesna, M W Vevers, Brian Viles, Henry Villiers, Carole Vincent, Dorothy F Vincent, Erika Vincent, Anne Viner, Patsy Vinton, Heather Vipers, Book Visitors, Kathy Vivian, Emmeline Vizard, Daniel Vizard-Williams, Der Von;

Jeff Waddell, Jason Waid, Sue Waine, Martin Wainwright, Penny Wainwright, Bruce Waite, Helen Waite, Ruth Wake, Aimee Wakelin, Alex Walker, Amy Walker, Anthony Walker, Brian Walker, Chris Walker, Ian Walker, Katherine Walker, Peter Walker, Valerie Walker, Ina Wallace, Lindsey Waller, Matthew Wallis, Angela Walters, Bethany Walters, Martin Walters, Eleanor Ward, Jackie Ward, Jacqui Ward, Lynn Ward, Martina Ward, Neil Ward, Rachel Ward, Ruth Ward, Sheena Ward, Zietta Ward, Judith Wardle, John Ward-Smith, Paul Warham, Emily Warne, Andrea Warner, George Warner, Heather Warner, Mike Warner, Zara Warner, Claire Warren, John Erkki Warren, Keith Waterfall, Andrew Waterhouse, Huw Waters, Stuart Waters, Sarah Watkinson, Bethan Watson, David Watson, Dylan Watson, Marcia Watson, Alison Wattiau, A.B. Watts, Flavia Watts, Tim Watts, Nicola Waugh, Susan Weatherhead, Catherine Weaver, Helen Webb, Judy Webb, Oliver Webb, Ronald Webb, Karen Websdale, C Webster, Diane Webster, Anne Marie Welch, Sue Welch, Chris Wells, Manon Welter, Jill Wennberg, Sarah Werts, Betty West, Carly West, Julia West, Katie West, Silvia West, Steve West, Helen Westlake, Jill Westmacott, P Westmore, Elizabeth Weston, Donna Whaley, Nigel Wharton, Marie Whatmough, Chris Whear, Jane Wheeler, Richard Wheeler, Roger Whelan, Peter Whipp, Felicity Whitaker, Terry Whitaker, Adrian White, Alex White, Carole White, Chris White, David J White, Debbie White, Edwin White, Jon White, Jonathan White, Marion White, Mark White, Mary White, Paul White, Peter White, Margaret Whitfield, Catherine Whiting, Pauline Whiting, Sarah Whiting, Ashley Whitlock, Joan Whittaker, John Whittaker, Cathy Whittle, Nicola Whittle, Matt Why, Carey Widdows, Alan Wilcockson, Jenny Wilcockson, Katie Wilcox, Tim Wilcox, Liz Wild, David Wilding, Jayne Wilesmith, Colin Wiliams, Barbara Wilkins, Mike Wilkins, Malcolm Wilkinson, Mike Wilkinson, Ann Willan, Jackie Willcox, Anne Williams, Bryan Williams, Carla Williams, Colin Williams, David Williams, Janice Williams, Judith Williams, Lesley Williams, Nicholl Williams, Raine Williams, Sally Williams, Suzanne Williams, Zoe Williams, Kathryn Williamson, Sally Williamson, David Willis, Alan Willison, Lynn Willmott, Trudy Willows, Anthea Wilson, Derek Wilson, Emma Wilson, Ian Wilson, Jean Wilson, Ken Wilson, Maz Wilson, Ray & Liz Wilson, Richard Wilson, Tony Wilson, Wendy Wilson, David L Wilton, Vikki Wimbridge, Barbie Wimbury, Liz Windmill, Faye Winfield, Valerie Wing, Nigel Winser, Bryan Winsley, Martin Wise, Sue Witcomb, Andrea Wood, Andrew Wood, Dawn Wood, Elaine Wood, Jane Wood, Judy Wood, Karl Wood, Neil Wood, Nick Wood, Poppy Wood, Terry Wood, Daw Woode, Becky Woodell, Dominic Woodfield, Mila Woodfield, Frankie Woodgate, Paul Woodham, Rebecca Woodman-Halford, Chris Woodrow, Aaron Woods, Edy Woods, Hannah Woods, Val Woods, Alice Woodward, Alan Woolard, Ian Wooldridge, Lorna Woolhouse, Sarah Woolhouse, Maureen Woollacott, Steve Woollard, Steve Woolliams, Christine Wormald, Paul Worth, Sue Worthington, Emma Wray-Smith, Antonia Wrenn, Ann Wright, Anthea Wright, Brian Wright, Frances Wright, Heather Wright, Ivan Wright, Joe Wright, John Wright, Jonathan Wright, Mike Wright, David Wright, Paula Wright, Ulrike Wright, Pamela Wrighton, Jenny Wylie, Ann Wyllie;

Yali Xue;

Anna Yalci, P Yates, Denise Yelland, Alistair Yeomans, Alice Young, Charlotte Young, Chris Young, Judith Young, Phillip Young, Rodney Young, Sharon Young, Jeff Youngman, R.E. Youngman; Diana Zatouroff.